J. WESTON
WALCH
PUBLISHER

Learning Skills for School, Home, & Work

Nancy Lobb

User's Guide
to
Walch Reproducible Books

Purchasers of this book are granted the right to reproduce all pages.

This permission is limited to a single teacher, for classroom use only.

Any questions regarding this policy or requests to purchase further reproduction rights should be addressed to

Permissions Editor
J. Weston Walch, Publisher
321 Valley Street • P.O. Box 658
Portland, Maine 04104-0658

1   2   3   4   5   6   7   8   9   10
ISBN 0-8251-4629-1
Copyright © 2003
J. Weston Walch, Publisher
P. O. Box 658 • Portland, Maine 04104-0658
walch.com
Printed in the United States of America

CONTENTS

To the Teacher

Learning Strategies for School, Home, and Work is a new lifestyle approach to teaching learning strategies. The skills your students will learn from this book are powerful tools that can change their lives. These learning strategies are not isolated skills to be used only in school. They are important skills students will use the rest of their lives at school, home, and work.

In *Learning Strategies for School, Home, and Work,* students will learn how to use their learning style to understand things more quickly and remember them better. They will learn how to set goals to give their lives direction and purpose. They will learn strategies to help them get things done with time to spare.

Students will learn how to get the information they need to make better decisions. They will learn a simple strategy to help them understand what they read, as well as note-taking strategies for many different situations. They will learn strategies to help them improve their memories. Finally, they will learn test-taking strategies that will improve their grades on every test.

Learning Strategies for School, Home, and Work is carefully organized for easy use by the teacher. Each chapter begins with a story about a young person who had a problem that was solved using a learning strategy. The learning strategy being taught in that chapter is then presented on the next several pages. The main idea of the page is written at the bottom and marked by the lightbulb symbol. Three application pages follow in which the student uses the skill at school, home, and work. These pages are marked by the symbols of a backpack, house, and hard hat respectively. Finally, a chapter test allows you to assess how well students have mastered the skill being taught.

Other features include a Learning Style Inventory (page 3) and two Learning Strategies Inventories (pages 126 and 130), which can serve as a pretest and posttest for the book. The Teacher's Guide (page 111) includes background information, a list of vocabulary to be taught, answers, and additional activities to extend the concepts being taught.

If your students work hard and master the skills featured in this book, they will see benefits throughout their lives at school, home, and work.

To the Student

In *Learning Strategies for School, Home, and Work,* you will learn about learning strategies. A general uses strategy to win a battle. A chess player uses strategy to win a game. A sports team uses strategy to beat the other team. A strategy is a plan, but not just any plan. It is a plan made with skill. You cannot have a good strategy unless you have skills!

So why is this book called *Learning Strategies*? That is because it teaches you the skills you need to make a plan for learning. These skills can change your life! If you use the strategies taught in this book, you will get better grades. Your home life will be more organized and enjoyable. And you will do better at work, getting promotions and higher pay.

Did you know that . . .
* strategies that use your learning style will allow you to learn things more quickly and remember them better?
* strategies toward a goal will give your life direction and purpose?
* strategies will help you get things done and have time to spare?
* strategies can help you get the information you need to make better decisions?
* a simple strategy will help you understand more of what you read?
* good note-taking strategies will make the difference between passing and failing?
* it is easy to learn strategies that improve your memory?
* learning a few test-taking strategies will improve your grade on every test?

As you read *Learning Strategies for School, Home, and Work,* you will find symbols to guide you. The lightbulb ( ) marks the main idea of a page. The backpack ( ) marks a page on which the skill is being used at school. The house ( ) marks a page on which the skill is being used at home. Finally, the hard hat ( ) marks a page on which the skill is being used at work.

 Remember, learning strategies are not just for school! They are important skills you will use all your life. Work hard to learn the skills presented in this book. Once you have learned them, put them into practice as often as you can. If you do this, your learning skills will become learning habits. They will serve you well at school, home, and work!

GETTING STARTED: USING YOUR LEARNING STYLE

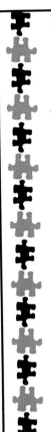

Tam sat down to do her homework. She had to learn 10 new words for English. There would be a test the next day.

Tam read the list of words over and over. It wasn't long before her eyes were just moving over the page. Soon her head was nodding. When her mother called Tam to dinner, she found Tam asleep.

The next day, Tam just couldn't remember the words. Her test grade was low. Tam stayed after class to talk to the teacher. "Those words are too hard. I can't learn all those in one night," Tam said.

Tam's teacher wanted to help. She gave Tam a test to see how she learned best. The test said Tam was an **auditory** learner. That meant she learned best by hearing.

The next week the teacher gave the class another word list. This time Tam knew what to do. She went home and made **flash cards.** Then she read the words and their meanings out loud. She did this many times. Then she read the words and their meanings into the tape recorder. She played the tape back over and over.

When the test came, Tam was ready. She remembered every word. It was easy because she used her **learning style.**

WHAT HAPPENED?

Tam learned the new words easier because she used her learning style. She studied in the way that was best for her.

WHAT DO YOU THINK?

1. Why do you think Tam had trouble studying for the first test?

2. Why do you think she did better on the second test?

① WHAT IS A LEARNING STYLE?

> Joy, Lil, and Bob each got the same new **computer** program. Joy sat down and read the instructions. Lil called a friend who knew how to use the program. Her friend came over and told Lil what to do. Bob started up the program and began playing around with it. It wasn't long before all three were happily using their new programs. But they had gone about it in very different ways.

Joy is a **visual** learner. Visual learners learn best by seeing what they want to learn. Visual learners like to see directions written down. They remember what they read. Visual learners study best by taking notes and then reading them over.

Lil is an **auditory** learner. Auditory learners learn best when they hear what they want to learn. Auditory learners remember what they hear. They remember things best by talking about information with another person. Reading aloud can help an auditory learner remember.

Bob is a **kinesthetic** learner. A kinesthetic learner learns best by doing. Kinesthetic learners like hands-on work. They learn best by using the information they are learning. They may like making a poster or project. They may need to get up and move around as they study.

Using your learning style can make your life easier. It can help you get better grades. It can help you remember better at home and work, too. You will find out more about how to use your learning style as you read this book.

You can find out your learning style. Take the inventory on pages 3 and 4. Read the questions carefully. There are no right or wrong answers.

Your score on the test will tell you if you learn best by seeing (visual), by hearing (auditory), or by doing (kinesthetic). Some people will have scores that are the same or very close on two learning styles. If that is true for you, you will need to study the hints for both learning styles and choose the ones that work for you. After all, the goal of studying about learning styles is for you to find out what will be helpful for you!

Remember, you may be a visual, auditory, or kinesthetic learner.

2 A LEARNING STYLE INVENTORY

Circle the number of each statement below that is true about you. There are no right or wrong answers. When you are finished, you will find out how to score your inventory on page 5.

1. I like to read.

2. I am good at sports.

3. I am good at puzzles and mazes.

4. I like to study with a friend.

5. I like to chew gum or eat a snack while I study.

6. I write things down over and over to remember them.

7. I would rather read the newspaper than listen to the news on the radio.

8. I like to write letters.

9. I like to talk on the telephone.

10. I like to talk about ideas more than reading about them.

11. I can watch someone do a dance step, then copy it.

12. I like to move around when I am studying.

13. I like music to study by.

14. I like directions to be written down.

15. I like to study alone.

16. I need quiet to study.

17. I learn more by listening to the teacher than by reading.

18. I can follow spoken directions better than written directions.

19. I can't work if it's too noisy or too quiet.

20. I study by reading over my notes.

21. I tap my foot or my hands when I study.

22. I like to act things out.

23. I like to look things up in the library.

24. I remember more by listening than by reading.

25. I like listening to the news on the radio more than reading the newspaper.

(continued)

2 A LEARNING STYLE INVENTORY (continued)

26. I like to work with tools.

27. I have trouble sitting still.

28. It's hard for me to work for a long time without talking.

29. Reading things out loud helps me remember better.

30. I like to write things down to remember them better.

31. I don't like to talk much.

32. I learn best by doing an activity or project.

33. I remember people's faces, not their names.

34. I move my lips when I read.

35. I learn best by trying things out for myself.

36. I learn best in a group.

37. I learn best through class discussions.

38. I like to explain my answers in class.

39. Noise or music bothers me when I study.

40. Pacing the floor helps me when I try to study.

41. I like to use an outline when I study.

42. I like to read new material out loud.

43. Music helps me concentrate when I study.

44. I like to underline important points when I read.

45. I like to do assignments with a friend.

46. I like to use a tape recorder to review important information.

47. Tapping my foot or fingers when I study helps me concentrate.

48. I study best sitting on the floor in a relaxed way.

49. I like to look things up in books.

50. I remember by picturing things in my mind.

51. I enjoy perfecting a movement in a sport or dance.

Now turn to the next page to score your inventory.

SCORING YOUR INVENTORY

Circle the numbers below that match the numbers you circled on pages 3 and 4. Then add the number of items you circled in each column. Count each circled number as 1. The column with the highest total tells you your learning style.

Visual (seeing)	Auditory (hearing)	Kinesthetic (doing)
1	4	2
3	9	5
7	10	6
8	17	11
14	18	12
15	19	13
16	24	21
20	25	22
23	28	26
30	29	27
31	34	32
33	36	35
39	37	40
41	38	43
44	42	47
49	45	48
50	46	51
Total:	Total:	Total:

Write the name of your learning style here: _____
(visual, auditory, or kinesthetic)

If your scores were the same or very close on two learning styles, you may have a mixed learning style. In this case, you will probably find that tips from both learning styles can help you.

On the next three pages, you will learn tips that help each type of learner. If you are a visual learner, you will find tips on page 6. But, what if you read the tips for auditory learners on page 7 and find something there that helps you? That is not a problem! The goal of all material on learning strategies is to help you think about what works for you. If you are a kinesthetic learner, you will find most of the tips on page 8 helpful. That does not mean that you should not use other tips that work for you. (Very few people are 100% visual and 0% auditory or kinesthetic.)

  walch.com © 2003 Walch Publishing

TIPS FOR THE VISUAL LEARNER

Visual learners learn best by seeing. If you are a visual learner, here are ways to make learning easier.

1. Write down things you want to remember.
2. Take notes. Read them over and over.
3. Make flash cards. Look at them over and over.
4. Study alone.
5. Study in a quiet place.
6. Underline or **highlight** main ideas. Read these many times.
7. Write notes. Cover them. Try to see them in your mind. Write them again.
8. Make **outlines** of important points.
9. Use charts, maps, and pictures to study.
10. Keep study materials neat.

WHAT DO YOU THINK?

1. Why would flash cards and notes help a visual learner?

2. Why might a visual learner prefer to do a written report rather than an oral report?

3. How might a visual learner best learn a list of vocabulary words?

 Remember, visual learners learn best by *seeing* information they need to learn.

5 TIPS FOR THE AUDITORY LEARNER

Auditory learners learn best by hearing. If you are an auditory learner, here are ways to make learning easier.

1. Listen carefully when information is explained.

2. Talk about the information with a friend.

3. Say information you want to remember out loud several times.

4. Make a tape of something you want to learn. Listen to it over and over.

5. When you read, stop and say out loud what each paragraph is about.

6. Make flash cards. Read them out loud as you study.

7. Read out loud when you can.

8. Have directions explained to you.

9. Study with a friend.

10. Underline or highlight main ideas. Read these out loud over and over.

WHAT DO YOU THINK?

1. Why might studying with a friend help an auditory learner?

2. Why might an auditory learner prefer to do an oral report rather than a written report?

3. How might an auditory learner best learn a list of vocabulary words?

 Remember, auditory learners learn best by _hearing_ information they need to learn.

6 TIPS FOR THE KINESTHETIC LEARNER

Kinesthetic learners learn best by doing. If you are a kinesthetic learner, here are ways to make learning easier.

1. Take many short breaks when studying. You might study 20 minutes and break for 5. Then get back to work.

2. Make flash cards. Put them in piles as you learn them.

3. If you can't sit still, try doing hand exercises. Or squeeze an exercise ball in your hand as you study.

4. At home, walk around when you try to memorize something.

5. You may not study best at a desk. Try out other spots, like the floor or a beanbag.

6. Study with music.

7. Act out what you are learning.

8. Type what you're learning on the computer.

9. Make a poster or project.

10. Eat a snack or chew gum while you study.

WHAT DO YOU THINK?

1. Why might taking many short breaks help a kinesthetic learner?

2. Why might a kinesthetic learner prefer to do a hands-on project rather than a report?

3. How might a kinesthetic learner best learn a list of vocabulary words?

 Remember, kinesthetic learners learn best by *doing*.

7 **USING YOUR LEARNING STYLE AT SCHOOL**

Circle the letter of the best answer(s). There may be more than one correct answer.

> Assignment #1
> Learn how to spell a list of 20 words correctly.

1. A visual learner should
    a. write the words, then cover them and write them again.
    b. make flash cards and look at them over and over.
    c. underline hard parts of the words.
    d. spell the words out loud.

2. An auditory learner should
    a. spell the words out loud.
    b. study the words with a friend.
    c. walk around the room while studying.
    d. read the words silently.

3. A kinesthetic learner should
    a. type the words on a computer.
    b. take many breaks while studying.
    c. walk around the room while studying.
    d. sit at a desk and look at the words silently.

> Assignment #2
> Study for a test.

4. A visual learner should
    a. take notes and read them over and over.
    b. study with a friend.
    c. underline or highlight main ideas.
    d. study alone in a quiet place.

5. An auditory learner should
    a. take notes and read them out loud.
    b. tape important ideas and listen to them over and over.
    c. read notes silently.
    d. walk around while reading notes.

6. A kinesthetic learner should
    a. do hand exercises while studying.
    b. eat a snack or chew gum while studying.
    c. make a poster outlining main ideas.
    d. try to sit quietly for two or three hours at a time.

8 USING YOUR LEARNING STYLE AT HOME

Al, Joe, and Amy own the same kind of lawn mower. The **air filter** on each mower needs to be cleaned. Read the directions below. Then answer the questions.

Cleaning the Air Filter on Your Mower

Clean the air filter every 50 hours of use.
Clean it more often if there is a lot of dust.
Do not use the mower without the filter. You will damage the mower.

1. Snap open the air-filter cover.
2. Take off the air filter.
3. Wash the air filter in **laundry detergent.**
4. Squeeze out extra water. Dry the filter with a paper towel.
5. Put one tablespoon of oil on the air filter.
6. Squeeze the filter to spread the oil around.
7. Put the filter back. Close the air-filter cover.

1. Al is an auditory learner. What do you think he could do to better understand the directions?

2. Joe is a visual learner. What do you think he might do to better understand the directions?

3. Amy is a kinesthetic learner. What do you think she might do to better understand the directions?

4. Why do you think it would be important to follow the directions when cleaning the filter?

9 USING YOUR LEARNING STYLE AT WORK

Maria, Jill, and Lin were hired to **stock** shelves in a grocery store. Their job is to keep the shelves full. Each **aisle** in the store has a number. Maria, Jill, and Lin have to learn the aisle numbers for each item in the store. That way, they will know where to put new items. They can also help customers who are looking for an item.

Super Food Layout

Aisle 1	meat, fish	Aisle 2	milk, eggs, cheese
Aisle 3	soap, brooms, wax	Aisle 4	coffee, tea, juice, cereal
Aisle 5	bread, crackers	Aisle 6	nuts, gum, chips, candy
Aisle 7	mustard, catsup	Aisle 8	salad dressing, oil
Aisle 9	soup, fruit, vegetables	Aisle 10	jam, peanut butter, syrup
Aisle 11	flour, sugar, spices	Aisle 12	paper goods
Aisle 13	frozen foods	Aisle 14	fresh produce

1. Maria is a visual learner. How do you think she might use her visual sense to help her learn the aisles?

2. Jill is a kinesthetic learner. How do you think she might learn the aisles by doing something active?

3. Lin is an auditory learner. How do you think he might use his sense of hearing to help him learn the aisles?

4. Why do you think each of these workers should learn where things go on the aisles as quickly as possible?

⑩ USING YOUR LEARNING STYLE TEST

Write **True** or **False** by each sentence below. If the sentence is false, rewrite it correctly in the space below the sentence.

_____ 1. An auditory learner learns best by hearing.

_____ 2. All people learn by doing things the same way.

_____ 3. Learning will be easier if you use your learning style.

_____ 4. Kinesthetic learners do not like hands-on work.

_____ 5. Visual learners do not like to read directions.

_____ 6. Reading out loud can help an auditory learner remember.

_____ 7. Kinesthetic learners should never move around when they study.

_____ 8. A visual learner should study alone in a quiet place.

_____ 9. A visual learner should write down things to remember.

_____ 10. Auditory learners should only read silently.

_____ 11. A kinesthetic learner should not take study breaks.

(continued)

⑩ USING YOUR LEARNING STYLE TEST *(continued)*

_____ 12. An auditory learner may learn best when studying with a friend.

_____ 13. Some kinesthetic learners need to move around while studying.

_____ 14. Playing a tape of material to be learned can help an auditory learner.

_____ 15. A visual learner should never use a highlighter.

_____ 16. Visual learners usually prefer to do an oral report rather than a written report.

_____ 17. Auditory learners do better in school than visual or kinesthetic learners.

_____ 18. No one should ever study to music.

_____ 19. You only need to use your learning style in school.

_____ 20. Finding out your learning style can make your life easier.

_____ 21. Kinesthetic learners learn best by doing.

_____ 22. Auditory learners may learn best by reading out loud.

_____ 23. A person may have a mixed learning style.

_____ 24. It is hard to find out your learning style.

_____ 25. Using your learning style may help you improve your grades.

CHAPTER 1: SETTING GOALS FOR YOURSELF

Jen and Molly hoped to be child-care workers when they finished school. Both girls liked children. A new day-care center was opening in a year. It would be a great job.

Jen signed up for a course in child care. She worked hard and learned all she could. Some weekends, Jen babysat for neighbors. She did a good job. The parents were happy with her work.

Molly did not take the child-care course. It sounded like too much work. She was too busy with friends to babysit on weekends. She thought Jen was silly for working so hard.

When the new day-care center opened, Jen was hired. She got good pay and a nice place to work. Molly was turned down. She couldn't understand why. She used to be just as good at child care as Jen.

WHAT HAPPENED?

Jen set a goal for herself. Then she worked hard to reach her goal. Molly did not set a goal. She drifted along having fun.

WHAT DO YOU THINK?

1. How did having a goal affect what Jen did with her time?

2. How do you think working toward a goal might give your life direction?

3. Why do you think different people might have different goals?

4. Have you ever set a goal for yourself? If so, what was it? Did you reach your goal?

MAKING A GOAL

WHAT IS A GOAL?

A **goal** is something you want to do. Goals give your life purpose and direction. With a goal, you know what you are doing and why.

There are three things to think about when you set a goal for yourself.

1. A goal should be something that is **important** to you. It should be something you really want to do. A goal should be something you are willing to work hard to reach. If your goal is important, you will not forget about your goal when other things come up to distract you.

2. A goal should be **specific.** A specific goal is stated clearly and in detail. It should be easy to tell when you have reached the goal. For example, a goal to "get better at shooting baskets" is not specific. (How will you know when you are "better"?) A goal to average 8 out of 10 free shots is specific. (You'll know when you can do this!)

3. A goal should also be **realistic.** That means it should be within your reach. You should have a good chance of reaching it with hard work.

> A goal that is right for you should be
> - important to you
> - specific, and
> - realistic.

WHAT DO YOU THINK?

Read each goal. Answer the questions.

1. Kay makes $15 a week. She has no other money saved. Her goal is to buy a new computer and printer next week. Kay's goal is important to her. It is specific. But why is it not a realistic goal right now?

2. Lou's goal is to get along better with his boss. Lou's goal is important to him. It is realistic. But it is not specific. How do you think Lou could make his goal more specific?

 Remember, a goal should be important, specific, and realistic.

SHORT- AND LONG-TERM GOALS

Studying for the next hour. Cleaning your apartment. Finishing a book by Monday. All of these goals are **short-term goals.** They can be reached in short periods of time such as hours, days, or maybe weeks.

Long-term goals take months or years to reach. Graduating from high school is a long-term goal. Buying a car is another.

Long-term goals usually need to be broken down into several short-term goals. For example, maybe your goal is to pass algebra. That is a long-term goal. It can be broken down into these short-term goals: passing each test, doing each assignment.

TRY IT OUT!

Write **short** or **long** on the line by each goal below:

_____ 1. to learn how to play the piano well
_____ 2. to pass the G.E.D. test
_____ 3. to become a carpenter
_____ 4. to pass the history test tomorrow
_____ 5. to help your grandmother with her shopping after school
_____ 6. to get a job that pays well
_____ 7. to wash your car today
_____ 8. to help your friend study for a test

WHAT DO YOU THINK?

11. What is your goal for this week?

12. What are your goals for this year?

13. What are your goals for five years from now?

 Remember, short-term goals can be reached in short periods of time. Long-term goals take months or years to reach.

3 STEPS TO REACHING YOUR GOAL

Once you set a goal for yourself, you need a plan to reach it. Here are the steps to take:

1. Write down your goal. Make sure it is important to you, specific, and realistic.
2. Put the paper where you will see it daily. This will help you keep **focused** on working toward your goal.
3. List the steps needed to reach the goal.
4. Work toward your goal.

Many goals need to be broken down into steps. You may be able to decide on these steps yourself. Or you may need to get help. For example, if your goal is to get a passing grade in English, you could ask the teacher to help you make a plan. If your goal is to learn to swim across the pool, you could find steps in a book for learning how to swim. You could take lessons. Or you could ask a friend who swims well.

WHAT DO YOU THINK?

1. Why do you think it would be a good idea to write down your goal?

2. What is the purpose of seeing your written goal daily?

3. You set a goal of earning a "C" or higher on your science project. You are not sure how to do this. How could you get help deciding on the steps needed to reach your goal?

4. You set a goal of running a mile in under six minutes. You are not sure of the best way to improve your time. How could you get help deciding on the steps needed to reach your goal?

 Remember, write down your goal and the steps needed to reach it. Put the paper where you will see it daily.

4 BREAKING A LONG-TERM GOAL INTO STEPS

Mark was a high-school student. Mark's goal was to buy a used car. He thought he could find something nice for about $5,000.

Mark thought about his goal. He knew it was important to him. He was specific about what he wanted. And he thought it was realistic. Mark wrote down his goal and posted it on the bathroom mirror.

When Mark tried to break his goal down into steps, he had trouble. So he got some help. He talked to a car dealer. And he spoke to the credit union where he and his parents had savings accounts.

Buying a car is a big step. Mark was smart to think it through. After talking to his parents, the car dealer, and the credit union, Mark broke his goal into these steps:

1. **Estimate** monthly expenses for owning a car that costs $5,000.
   a. Find out what the monthly payments will be on a car loan.
   b. Find out how much the insurance will cost per month.
   c. Find out how much gas will cost per month.
2. Save enough money to pay for the license plate.
3. Save $25 every month toward future repairs.
4. Find out what kinds of cars cost $5,000.
5. Shop around for the best deal.

WHAT DO YOU THINK?

1. Mark found out that the payments on a three-year car loan at 8% interest will be about $175 per month. The insurance will cost about $150 per month. He estimated $60 per month for gas. He planned to put aside $25 per month for repairs. What was Mark's total estimated monthly cost?

2. Mark earned $6 per hour at the grocery store. He worked 15 hours a week (60 hours a month). How much did Mark earn in a month?

3. Mark found out his goal was not realistic. How could he change his goal to make it more realistic?

Remember, a long-term goal must be broken into steps.

5 SETTING A GOAL AT SCHOOL

Tyrone and Ted wanted to be on the track team at school. Both could run fast. But Ted always beat Tyrone when they raced at home. The tryouts were in six weeks.

Tyrone wrote down his goal on a note card. He taped the card on his mirror. He talked to the track coach about how to improve. He read a book about running. He made a list of the steps he should take to improve. And he ran five miles every day after school.

Ted knew he was a good runner. He knew he'd make the team. He couldn't believe Tyrone was wasting time reading books and working out.

The tryouts came. Tyrone made the team, and Ted did not. Ted wondered how Tyrone had gotten so fast.

WHAT DO YOU THINK?

1. Tyrone had a goal. Do you think that was the only reason he made the team?

2. Why do you think it helped Tyrone to tape his goal on his mirror?

3. Why do you think talking to the track coach was a good idea?

4. What steps do you think Tyrone might list to help him reach his goal?

6 SETTING A GOAL AT HOME

 Greg rented his first apartment. It was small, but the rent was low. It was in a good neighborhood close to work. But the apartment was run-down. It needed to be painted. The **landlord** said he would pay for the paint if Greg did the work. Greg did not know how to paint. He set a goal to learn how to paint so he could do the work.

Circle the letter of the best answer.

1. What is the first thing Greg should do?
   a. Buy paint.
   b. Find a new apartment.
   c. Write down his goal.
   d. Give up. Painting is too hard.

2. Which is NOT a good way to find out how to paint?
   a. Read a book about how to paint.
   b. Just start in. It can't be that hard.
   c. Get advice from a store that sells paint.
   d. Get advice from a friend who works as a painter.

3. Painting the apartment is a long-term goal. Greg should
   a. break the long-term goal into smaller short-term goals.
   b. quit. It will take too long to finish.
   c. try to finish as quickly as possible.
   d. only paint one room.

WHAT DO YOU THINK?

4. List steps you think Greg should take to reach his goal. Number the steps in the order you think he should do them.

5. Do you think Greg's goal is realistic? Explain.

7 SETTING A GOAL AT WORK

 Val graduated from high school in May. She was hired as a file clerk in a big law firm. She likes her job. And she likes where she works. But her job pays **minimum wage.** Val hopes to work her way up to a high-paying job as a **legal secretary.** Her goal is to do this in five years.

Getting a job as a legal secretary is a long-term goal. Put an X in front of each thing Val might do to help her reach her long-term goal.

_____ 1. See if another law firm will hire her as a legal secretary now.

_____ 2. Sign up for a class in word processing.

_____ 3. Buy a new car.

_____ 4. Write down her goal and post it on the mirror in her bedroom.

_____ 5. Make a list of the steps needed to reach her goal.

_____ 6. Look for a bigger apartment.

_____ 7. Find out what training is needed to become a legal secretary.

_____ 8. Learn as much as she can about her present job.

_____ 9. Ask for a raise.

_____ 10. Take classes in office skills on the weekends.

_____ 11. Give up. It's not a realistic goal.

_____ 12. Do her best work on the job she has now.

_____ 13. Do extra jobs at work to learn more about how the law firm works.

_____ 14. **Volunteer** to help one of the legal secretaries.

_____ 15. Let everyone at work know how boring her job is.

_____ 16. Get along well with others at work.

WHAT DO YOU THINK?

17. What do you think is the most important thing Val should do to reach her goal? Why?

USING YOUR LEARNING STYLE TO REACH YOUR GOALS

You can use your learning style to help you reach your goals. Here are a few suggestions:

Visual Learner

Visual learners might write about their goals in their journals. They might write a story about their goals. Or they might make a sign to remind them of their goals.

Auditory Learner

Auditory learners might talk with others about their goals. They might tape-record their goals and play the tape regularly. They might set goals together with a friend.

Kinesthetic Learner

Kinesthetic learners might make a chart or picture illustrating their goals. They could act out reaching their goals.

Write your learning style here: _____

(visual, auditory, or kinesthetic)

Now answer each question below.

1. Name a goal you have for yourself in school. How do you think you could use your learning style to reach that goal?

2. Name a goal you have for yourself at home. How do you think you could use your learning style to reach that goal?

3. Name a goal you have for yourself at work (or for a future job). How do you think you could use your learning style to reach that goal?

9 CHAPTER TEST

Answer the questions below.

1. Your friend wants to know the difference between short-term and long-term goals. How can you explain it?

2. Your long-term goal is to finish high school. What would be some good short-term goals to help you?

3. Why do you think your goals should be specific?

4. Why do you think your goals should be realistic?

5. Why do you think it is important to set goals?

6. What are some things that could get in the way of reaching a goal?

7. What could you do if your goal seems out of reach?

8. Why do you think some people seem to get more done than others?

9. Why do you think some people might give up on their goals?

10. Why might the same goal not be right for everyone?

CHAPTER 2: GETTING ORGANIZED

Shanika had too much to do. She had a big test in biology the next day. Soccer tryouts were from 4 P.M. to 6 P.M. Her friends were all going to the opening of the new mall. Shanika needed to wash her car. And she planned to get a haircut for the dance on Friday night.

After school was out at 3 P.M., Shanika went into high gear. She stopped at the car wash. Then she got her hair cut. While she was there, she got her nails done. Then Shanika met her friends at the mall. She got home at 9 P.M.

Shanika's mom was not happy. "You promised to pick up your brother after school today. I had to leave work early to get him. By the way, how did the soccer tryouts go?"

"I forgot!" said Shanika. "I just have too much to do. And I haven't had any time to study for my biology test, either."

WHAT HAPPENED?

Shanika is not well **organized.** She needs to learn how to organize her day so that the most important things get done. She was busy, but the things she did could have waited until another day. There was no time left for the most important things.

WHAT DO YOU THINK?

1. How do you think being better organized could help Shanika reach her goals?

2. Why do you think the order in which you do jobs might make a difference in how much you get done?

3. What do you think were the most important jobs Shanika had to do?

4. Which of Shanika's jobs could have been left for another day?

1 PLANNING YOUR TIME

Planning your time can help you reach your goals. Planning your time does not mean planning every minute of the day. It means thinking about what you need to do most. Those are the things you should get done first. If you have extra time, you can think about time for other things you'd like to do. Here's a good way to plan your time:

1. Make a To Do list of what you *need* to do.
2. To that list, add other things you'd *like* to do if you have time.
3. Decide which things on the list are the most important to do *and* must be finished that day. Next to those things, write **1**.
4. Next to other things that are important but are not due that day, write **2**.
5. Next to things that are not so important and can be done later, write **3**.

The things you mark **1** are important things that must be done that day. Studying for a test the next day is a **1**. Completing work that is due is a **1**. Doing daily chores or jobs is a **1**.

Things you mark **2** are important things that need to be worked on but are not due that day. If a paper or project is due in three days, it is a **2**. You need to work on it when you have finished the things marked **1**.

Things you mark **3** are things that can wait. Going to a movie or the store can usually wait. Going out with friends may have to wait until the weekend.

WHAT DO YOU THINK?

Read each item on the To Do list below. Mark each item **1**, **2**, or **3**.

_____ 1. Start working on the English paper that is due in five days.

_____ 2. Pick up bread and milk at the store for your mom, who is ill.

_____ 3. Go to the final day of football tryouts (required to make the team).

_____ 4. Get a new CD that just came out.

_____ 5. Study for the Spanish test tomorrow.

_____ 6. Go to the movies with a friend.

_____ 7. Go shopping for new clothes for school.

 Remember, a To Do list will help you get things done.

2 MAKING A DAILY SCHEDULE

You have learned how to make a To Do list. You have learned how to decide which things on your list should be done first. Now you will learn how to make a daily **schedule** to help you use your time well. A daily schedule shows what you need to do each day. It also shows when you plan to do it.

When you make a schedule, think about how much time each job will take. Be realistic. If you do not give yourself enough time, your schedule will not work.

Be sure you remember your goals as you write your schedule. Make time for working toward your goals every day if possible.

Here is how to write a daily schedule:

1. Write the day or date at the top of the schedule.
2. On the left, write the times you have for doing things.
3. By each time, write the job you plan to do.

TRY IT OUT!

1. Make a schedule for Ana. Start the schedule after school hours. Ana needs to study for a history test for two hours. She will eat dinner and take a break between 6 P.M. and 7 P.M. She gets out of school at 3 P.M. Basketball practice is from 4 P.M. to 5:30 P.M. She needs to get math tutoring after school at 3 P.M.

Ana's Schedule for Monday

Time	Job
3:00 P.M. – 4:00 P.M.	

2. One of Ana's goals is to bring up her history and math grades to a "C" or higher. How is her schedule above helping her reach that goal?

 Remember, a schedule will help you use your time well and work toward your goals.

3 USING A CALENDAR

Rosa has too many things to keep track of. She has three job **interviews** this week. She has a dentist **appointment.** She has an eye exam. She has a book due at the library. Her car needs a new license plate. She needs to pay her rent on time. (Last month she was late and got a late fee.)

There are too many **deadlines.** Rosa doesn't know how anyone could remember so many dates!

Rosa needs to get a **calendar.** She should put it where she will see it every day. She can write dates and deadlines on the calendar. If she does this every time something comes up, she will always know what she has to do. She can add the things on her calendar to her To Do list for the next day.

Here is one week from Rosa's January calendar:

Sunday	Monday	Tuesday	Wednesday	Thursday	Friday	Saturday
	3:00 interview at Smith's 4:30 dentist	rent due 4:00 eye exam	3:30 interview at May Auto Pay license-plate fee.	book due 4:00 interview at Miller Hardware	7:00 movies Goal: Have a job by today.	Help Pat move. 8:00 dinner with Frank

Before Rosa had a calendar, she got mixed up. Sometimes she forgot things she needed to do. Now she writes everything on the calendar. She does not have to work hard to remember everything. She just looks at her calendar.

Rosa also writes goals and the dates she would like to reach them on the calendar. That helps her keep focused on reaching her goals.

WHAT DO YOU THINK?

1. Why do you think a calendar can help you keep track of what you need to do?

2. Where do you think you would put a calendar so you would see it every day and remember what you have to do?

 Remember, a calendar will help you remember dates and deadlines.

4 ORGANIZING YOUR SPACE

Jobs at school, home, and work will go better if you organize your space. You will save time if you have everything you need in one place. You will be able to find things you need right away. Stopping to look for tools or materials is a waste of time. Your work will get done more quickly and easily if you are organized.

Here are some tips for getting organized:

At school

1. Write all assignments in one assignment notebook.
2. Have a different colored folder for each class. Put all your papers in the right folder.
3. Get organized for the next day before you go to bed. Put everything in your backpack. Make sure you have everything you need in one place.

At home

1. Have a place for everything. Put things back after you use them.
2. Keep papers in file folders. On the tab of each folder, write what is in it.
3. Go through drawers and closets to keep them organized. Throw out what you no longer use.

At work

1. Keep your desk or work area neat. Keep things in the same order so you can find them when you need them.
2. Put things in order at the end of each day.

WHAT DO YOU THINK?

1. How can you use the tips above to get better organized for school?

2. How can you use the tips above to get better organized at home?

3. Why do you think it would be important to be organized at work?

5 ▶ AVOIDING TIME WASTERS

Luis's boss asked him to organize the storeroom. She told Luis to open the boxes of new supplies. Then he was to put everything in its place on the shelves. The job was to be finished by the end of that day.

Luis looked at the mess in the storeroom. Then he left to get a snack. He told all his friends what a big job he had. Then he went back to the storeroom. He left to get a box cutter. By the time he found one, it was time for lunch.

After lunch, Luis opened a few boxes. He got **interrupted** by some phone calls. By the end of the day, most of the mess was still there. Luis's boss was not happy. "But I've been working on it all day," Luis answered.

WHAT HAPPENED?

Luis did work on the job he was given. But he wasted most of his day. Luis needs to learn how to **avoid** wasting time.

1. Avoid interruptions. They can keep you from getting a job done.
2. Make sure you understand directions before starting a job. That way you won't have to do it over.
3. Get all the supplies you need to do the job before you start working.

WHAT DO YOU THINK?

1. Put an X by each thing below that could interrupt your work.

_____ talking on the telephone   _____ watching television

_____ getting a snack   _____ talking to a friend

_____ looking out the window   _____ daydreaming

_____ looking for a lost assignment   _____ forgetting the assignment

2. What is the main way *you* waste time when you need to be studying?

 Remember, wasting time can keep you from finishing your work.

6 GETTING ORGANIZED AT SCHOOL

Chris and Jess were ninth-grade students. Both took the same classes with the same teachers. They had the same homework assignments and the same tests.

At school, Chris always had a pencil and paper. He had his homework ready to turn in. At home, Chris spent about an hour a night doing homework. He knew what he had to do because it was written in his assignment notebook. He had a separate folder for each class so he could find his papers in his backpack. He checked his assignment notebook at school and brought home the books he'd need to do his work.

At school, Jess dug through his backpack to find a pencil and paper. Sometimes he got a zero because he couldn't find his homework. At home, Jess spent all evening doing his homework. Often, he had to call someone to get the assignments. To find things in his backpack, he had to dump it out and dig through the mess. Sometimes he had to go to a friend's house to borrow a book he'd forgotten.

WHAT HAPPENED?

Chris kept his backpack organized. He put assignments in his assignment notebook so they were all in one place. He had a folder for each class and put papers for the class in it. That way he knew just where to look for everything. Chris also had a small pocket in his backpack where he kept pencils and a calculator. He had another place to keep notebook paper. His supplies were easy to find.

Jess's backpack was a mess. He just threw everything into it. So he had to dig through piles of old papers to find each thing he needed. He made a lot of trips to friends' houses to borrow things he'd forgotten to bring home. Jess dumped notebook paper and pencils into the bottom of his backpack. It was not easy to find them when he needed them!

Jess knew he needed to make a change. Chris explained his system to Jess. Right away, Jess's work went much more quickly. And it was easier for him, too.

WHAT DO YOU THINK?

1. What do you think you could do to better organize your backpack for school?

2. Why do you think being organized helps you use your time better?

GETTING ORGANIZED AT HOME

To do a good job studying at home, you need a good study spot. Here is how to make yourself a good spot to study:

1. Keep all the supplies you will need on the desk or table.
2. Keep the desk or table neat.
3. Sit in a comfortable chair that has a straight back.
4. The spot should be quiet. There should be no television, loud music, or phone. There should be no people coming through.
5. Have a good lamp that lights the whole table or desk.

WHAT DO YOU THINK?

Put an X by each thing that should be included in a good study spot.

_____ 1. a pencil holder with pens and sharpened pencils

_____ 2. a tape dispenser

_____ 3. a study lamp

_____ 4. a stack of comic books

_____ 5. a dictionary

_____ 6. a chair with a straight back

_____ 7. a television set

_____ 8. a refrigerator

_____ 9. toys for children you are babysitting

_____ 10. a radio

_____ 11. paper

_____ 12. a telephone

_____ 13. a bean bag chair

_____ 14. many people to keep you company

_____ 15. a desk or table

8 GETTING ORGANIZED AT WORK

 Marta worked in a large business. Her job was to answer the phone and take **messages.** Marta knew it was important to get every message right.

Marta made a form to use for messages. It had space for
1. the time and date of the call
2. the name of the person the call is for
3. the message, and
4. the name and number of the person calling
5. the name of the person who took the message.

TRY IT OUT!

Write each message on the pad. Use your name as the person taking the message.

Date:

Time:

To:

Message:

From (name, number):

Person taking message:

Mike Marks called at 8:15 A.M. on May 5 to set up a time for a business lunch with Jeff Clem. Call him at home 555-4455 or work 555-3423.

Date:

Time:

To:

Message:

From (name, number):

Person taking message:

Carlos's brother is ill. He has been taken to River Hospital. The call was from his mom. She has gone to the hospital. The number there is 555-3509. Time of call: January 23 at 4:15 P.M.

9 USING YOUR LEARNING STYLE TO GET ORGANIZED

You can use your learning style to help you get organized. Here are a few suggestions:

Visual learner

Visual learners will find written To Do lists, schedules, and calendars very helpful. They should organize their things carefully to make them look neat and to avoid distractions.

Auditory learner

Auditory learners might review their To Do lists, schedules, and calendars to themselves out loud. They might review them with a friend. They may wish to have a tape recorder in their work area.

Kinesthetic learner

Kinesthetic learners might make a chart or pictures to remind them what they have to do. They should organize their space to allow freedom to move around when working.

Write your learning style here: _____
(visual, auditory, or kinesthetic)

Now answer each question below.

1. How do you think you could use your learning style to help you plan your time?

2. How do you think you could use your learning style to help you organize your study area at home?

3. How do you think you could use your learning style to help you be better organized at school?

⑩ CHAPTER TEST

Write **Yes** or **No** on the line to tell if each is a good way to be organized. Explain your answer in the space below each item.

_____ 1. Make a list of all the jobs you want to do tomorrow. Then do the jobs in the order in which you wrote them.

_____ 2. Make a plan for every five minutes of the day. Try to follow it exactly.

_____ 3. Make a schedule. Think about how much time each job would take as you make the plan.

_____ 4. Make a list of jobs you need to do. Number them in order of importance.

_____ 5. Hang a calendar on the refrigerator. Write dates and deadlines on it.

_____ 6. Write assignments on scraps of paper and throw them in your backpack.

_____ 7. Put your backpack and the things you will need for school the next day in the same place every night before you go to bed.

_____ 8. Have a different colored folder for each class. Keep all papers for each class in the right folder.

CHAPTER 3: KNOWING WHERE TO GET INFORMATION

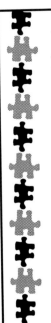

Julio and Rita Ortez had just moved to a new town. Julio was starting a new job. They had a small apartment. But they didn't know how to get the **utilities** turned on.

Rita had graduated from high school. She planned to go to **community college.** She wanted to become a nurse. Rita had a **learning disability** in reading that made reading hard for her. She wanted to learn more about that, so she could do her best in school.

Julio and Rita did not have a car. They needed to find out how to get around. They also needed to find a bank to set up a checking account.

Julio liked to play soccer. Rita hoped to find a bird-watching club. They wondered if they would be able to find anything to do in their new town.

Julio and Rita were worried. They wondered how they would get all the information they needed.

WHAT HAPPENED?

Julio and Rita needed to learn how to use the **resources** in their community. A resource is something that can be used for support or help. Every town has resources that can help. They needed to learn what these are and how to use them. When they learn to use the resources available to them, they will be happier in their new home.

In this chapter, you will learn about resources you can use to get information. It is not always an easy job. Sometimes you will have to look in more than one place. You will have to be willing to ask questions. Learning to make the most of your resources will make your life easier.

WHAT DO YOU THINK?

1. Every town has a telephone book and newspaper. What other resources do you think might be available in most towns?

2. Which of their needs do you think Julio and Rita needed to take care of first?

3. Which of their needs could wait until they were settled?

1 GETTING INFORMATION FROM THE TELEPHONE BOOK

The telephone book has a list of **community services.** It is found at the front of the white pages. This part of the phone book has numbers to call for help with many kinds of problems. Here is a sample Community Services page:

Automobile Information	**Health**
Driver's License 555-8837	Doctor referrals 555-4498
Car Tags 555-9965	American Red Cross 555-8375
Education	Madison Co. Hospital 555-8844
Jackson Schools 555-7753	**Libraries**
Madison Community College.......... 555-0087	Jackson Library............................. 555-3388
Olsen College 555-4213	**Transportation**
Emergency	Airport... 555-3211
All emergencies 911	Bus 555-9870
Government	Train 555-8405
City of Jackson 555-4356	**Utilities**
County of Madison 555-5567	Valley Gas..................................... 555-4938
State of Ohio................................. 555-4111	Jackson Electric 555-4998
U.S. Government........................... 555-4465	Bell West Phone 555-4903

TRY IT OUT!

Find the phone number you think would help in each case. Write it on the line.

1. Julio and Rita need a bus schedule. _____
2. Rita wants to get the electricity turned on. _____
3. Julio wants to find a dentist. _____
4. Rita wants to find out how to apply to the community college. _____
5. The Ortezes want to know when the city picks up garbage. _____
6. Rita wants to get a library card. _____
7. Julio wants to know how much it will cost to hook up a phone. _____
8. Rita wants to volunteer at the Red Cross. _____
9. Julio sees a fire across the street. _____

 Remember, the telephone book has information to help you solve many problems!

2 GETTING INFORMATION FROM THE NEWSPAPER

The newspaper is a great source of information. You can have the paper delivered to your home. You can buy it at a store. Or you can read it for free at the library.

Some people buy the paper only on Sunday. The Sunday paper is the largest of the week. It contains extra stories and many ads.

The newspaper index is usually on the front page of the paper. It tells where to find information in the newspaper. The letter tells the section of the paper. The number tells the page. For example, "1C" means the first page of section C.

Business	1C	Food	1F
Calendar	3E	Movies	3E
City News	3B	**Opinion**	8A
Classifed Ads	1G	People	2A
Comics	4–5E	Sports	1D
Crossword	5E	State News	1B
Deaths	4B	TV Listings	4E

TRY IT OUT!

1. Look at the index above. On what page would you look to answer each question below?

    a. What time is Mr. Jones's funeral? _____

    b. What happened at the football game last night? _____

    c. What is happening in your favorite comic strip? _____

    d. Is there anything good on television tonight? _____

    e. Are there any good used cars to buy? _____

    f. What is the news from around the state? _____

2. Another name for classified ads is the want ads. Why do you think people read the want ads?

 Remember, the newspaper has up-to-date information on many topics.

3 GETTING INFORMATION AT THE LIBRARY

Rita Ortez wanted to learn more about learning disabilities. She went to the public library.

Rita wandered around. She looked in the dictionary. "Learning disability" was not in there. Rita looked in the encyclopedia. There was one paragraph. But it was not any help. She walked through the stacks of books, but she didn't see anything. She decided to try the **Internet.** She typed in "learning disability" and got 1,238,423 results.

Rita went home. She told Julio there was no information in the library about learning disabilities.

WHAT HAPPENED?

Rita needed to learn how to use the resources of the library. The information she needed was there. But she did not know how to find it.

WHAT DO YOU THINK?

1. How do you think a **librarian** might have helped Rita?

2. If Rita does not know how to get information in the library, how do you think a librarian might help her learn?

3. Libraries are funded by tax dollars. Do you think this is a good use of tax money? Explain your answer.

 Remember, the librarian can help you use the resources of the library.

4 GETTING INFORMATION FROM REFERENCE BOOKS

Reference books are books that give basic information. You will find examples of reference books below. Reference books are found in every library and cannot be checked out. Other important reference materials are newspapers and magazines. These two resources contain the most up-to-date information.

1. A **dictionary** tells what words mean and how to say them.
2. An **encyclopedia** has articles giving detailed information on a wide variety of subjects.
3. A **thesaurus** gives words that mean the same as the words listed. For example, if you look up *happy*, you will find *glad, joyful, cheerful*, etc.
4. An **atlas** is a book of maps.
5. An **almanac** is a book published every year. It has various lists, charts, and tables of useful information in a wide variety of fields.
6. Newspapers and magazines have many kinds of up-to-date information.

WHAT DO YOU THINK?

Tell where you would look to find information to answer each question. Use the list of resources above.

1. Did the Bears win their football game last night? _____

2. How far is it from Miami to Boston? _____

3. What does the word *peon* mean? _____

4. Who was Booker T. Washington? _____

5. How do you say the word *queue?* _____

6. Where is the country of Egypt located? _____

7. What's the latest news on your favorite pop star? _____

8. Who won the elections yesterday? _____

9. What's another word meaning *funny?* _____

10. What's the current population of Brazil? _____

 Remember, reference books give you information on many topics.

5 GETTING BOOKS IN THE LIBRARY

Each book in the library has a **call number** that tells where to find the book. The call number is found in the computer **catalog.** The same number is also found on the book.

If you know the author or title of the book you want, just type it into the computer catalog. You will get the call number for the book. If you are looking for a book by subject, type the subject into the computer. If you don't get what you want, try another name for your subject. You may need to ask the librarian for help.

Once you've got the call number, you can look for the book. **Nonfiction** books (books about real things) are placed on the shelves by number. **Fiction** books (stories) are placed in order on a different set of shelves. They are listed in **alphabetical** order by the author's last name. The call number for reference books starts with the letter "R." Reference books are kept on their own set of shelves.

WHAT DO YOU THINK?

1. What is the purpose of a call number?

2. What would you do if you typed in a subject and found no books on that subject?

3. Why do you think the same book is listed in the catalog three ways?

4. What do you think you should do if you have the call number for a book, but you can't find it on the shelves?

 Remember, library books are organized by call number.

GETTING INFORMATION FROM THE INTERNET

Finding the information you need on the Internet is easier if you know what to do. Type the topic you want to find out about in a **search engine,** such as Google. A list of **web sites** will pop up. Click on the one you want to read. It sounds easy, and it usually is. But a few problems can come up.

1. A **broad** topic, like *dog,* will give you too much information! **Narrow** your search. For example, type "setter."
2. You can also narrow your search by typing in two commands. For example, type "puppy + shots" to find out what shots your puppy needs.
3. Put **quotation marks** (" ") around subjects of more than one word.
4. A misspelled word will not give you the web sites you want.
5. Anyone can put information on the Internet. You can usually trust sites of a college, museum, or government agency to give you correct information.

WHAT DO YOU THINK?

1. Write a narrower topic for each broad topic below:

   a. actor

   b. football team

2. Write what you could type in a search engine to get information on the rules of football.

3. Marcus wrote a report on oxygen using a web site. His teacher said there were mistakes in the information. What happened?

 Remember, narrow your search to get the information you need from the Internet.

7 GETTING INFORMATION FROM PEOPLE

Other people can be a good source of information. You may need to ask more than one person before you find someone who has the information you need. Don't be afraid to ask. Most people are glad to help. Here are a few ideas to think about:

1. Handling your money: Your bank can give you information about checking and savings accounts. **Credit counselors** can help if you get into **debt.**
2. Taxes: You can get free help with taxes from the Internal Revenue Service (IRS). The library or other groups may offer free tax help.
3. Health: Ask your friends if they have a doctor or dentist they like.
4. Tutoring: Free **tutoring** may be available at the library or local schools. Your teacher or school counselor may know how to help you find this service.
5. Crisis: **Agencies** are set up to help with **shelter,** drug or alcohol problems, physical abuse, etc.
6. Jobs: If you're looking for work, let others know. It's the best way to find work. (Your state **employment agency** also helps people find jobs.)
7. A place to live: Let people know you're looking.
8. On the job: Coworkers and your boss are good sources of information on how to do your job.

WHAT DO YOU THINK?

1. Why do you think it would be a good idea to talk to more than one bank before setting up a checking account?

2. Why is letting others know you need work a good way to find a job?

3. You need extra tutoring in math. Why do you think you should talk to your teacher or counselor to get help?

> **Remember, other people have good information to share if you are willing to ask.**

8 GETTING INFORMATION AT SCHOOL

1. You need to write a report on the Vietnam War. Where do you think you could get information? List two resources you could use. Explain why you chose each resource.

   a.   b.

2. You just finished reading *Romeo and Juliet* for English. You would like to see the play on tape. Where do you think you could get a free tape to watch?

3. You need some help with biology. You ask your teacher, but she is not available for tutoring after school. Whom else could you ask for information?

4. You want to look up some information on the Internet. You don't have a computer at home. Name two places you might be able to use a computer.

   a.   b.

5. You need to make a poster on checking accounts for math. How do you think you could get information? List two resources you could use. Explain why you chose each one.

   a.   b.

6. Sometimes you play tennis with a friend, but you aren't very good at it. You want to find out how to be a better tennis player. How do you think you could learn more about tennis? List two things you could do.

   a.   b.

7. You want to be an artist. List two resources you think you might use to learn more about art as a career.

   a.   b.

43

9 GETTING INFORMATION AT HOME

1. You need to hire a plumber. You look in the phone book and see 20 plumbers listed. Your friend recently hired a plumber who did poor work. How do you think you could find someone who will do a good job?

2. You want to buy a television. Your friend bought one that stopped working after only a year. How do you think you could find a television that would last a long time?

3. You have filled out your income-tax form. You're not sure if you did it correctly. How do you think you could get free help?

4. You don't know how to cook. You looked in a recipe book. All the recipes look too hard. How do you think you could find some good, easy recipes to try?

5. You have a credit-card bill you can't pay. You think you need to learn more about managing your money. How do you think you could get some free information?

6. You need to find a larger apartment. You walked around your neighborhood, but you didn't see any For Rent signs. What are two other ways you could look for an apartment?

7. The election is this week. You've seen the ads on television for people running for office. You can't decide whom to vote for. How do you think you could get more information?

10 GETTING INFORMATION AT WORK

1. You are new on the job. How can you find out what to do if you're sick one day?

2. Your boss wants you to learn computer skills. How do you think you could find out about classes to take?

3. You have a new job in a warehouse. What do you think you should do if you have questions about how to do your job?

4. Your boss wants you to send a message by E-mail. You are not sure how to do it. How do you think you could find out?

5. You are looking for a new job. You have been to the state employment agency. Where else do you think you could look?

6. You are at a job interview. The interviewer asks if you have a **résumé** (an outline of your education and experience). You say that you do not. How could you find out how to write one before your next job interview?

7. You are filling out a job application at a large company. You aren't sure what one of the questions means. You were told not to leave any questions blank. How do you think you could find out what the question means?

USING YOUR LEARNING STYLE TO GET INFORMATION

You can use your learning style to help you get information. Here are a few suggestions:

Visual learner

Visual learners like to learn by reading information. To get information, use written resources, such as the telephone book, newspaper, Internet, and library.

Auditory learner

Auditory learners may like getting information from other people, either in person or on the phone. At the library, ask the librarian if you need help. You may wish to read written information out loud.

Kinesthetic learner

Kinesthetic learners might get information by going to people and talking to them directly. When reading written information, they may wish to move around. They may want to make a chart or draw a picture of their findings.

Write your learning style here: _____
                                                            (visual, auditory, or kinesthetic)
Now answer each question below.

1. You want to keep better informed about the national news. How do you think you could use your learning style to help you do this?

2. You need to find a job. How could you get information about jobs, using your learning style to help you?

3. You want to learn how to change the oil in your car. How could you use your learning style to help you get the information you need to do this job?

12 CHAPTER TEST

Write **True** or **False** on the line by each statement. Rewrite each false statement to make it true.

_____ 1. It's best not to ask anyone if you don't know what to do on the job.

_____ 2. A list of community services can be found in most phone books.

_____ 3. Another name for classified ads is want ads.

_____ 4. A librarian's only job is to check out books.

_____ 5. If you want to see a map of Texas, look in a thesaurus.

_____ 6. You can read the newspaper at the library.

_____ 7. Every book in the library is on the shelves in alphabetical order.

_____ 8. On the Internet, you may get too many web sites if you type in a broad topic.

_____ 9. All information on the Internet is correct.

_____ 10. The bank will charge a fee to give you information about checking accounts.

(continued)

12 **CHAPTER TEST** *(continued)*

_____ 11. Never let anyone know if you are looking for a job.

_____ 12. The Community Services page in the phone book is a list of church services.

_____ 13. A new almanac comes out every year.

_____ 14. Encyclopedias are the best place to find out how to say a word.

_____ 15. If the call number on a book starts with "R," you can't check it out.

_____ 16. Every book in the library has a call number except fiction books.

_____ 17. The librarian will show you how to find things in the library.

_____ 18. To avoid too much information when using the Internet, narrow your search.

_____ 19. The employee handbook is a good source of information on the job.

_____ 20. The state employment agency helps people find jobs.

_____ 21. The most up-to-date information on a topic can be found in an encyclopedia.

_____ 22. The only information in a dictionary is word meanings.

CHAPTER 4: GETTING INFORMATION FROM BOOKS

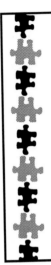

Keisha was writing a report for science. Her topic was **sonar.** Keisha did not know anything about sonar. Her teacher told her she would find it interesting. He told her that she could find some information in her science book. The report was due the next day.

That night, Keisha took a look at her science book. She opened the book and began flipping through it. An hour later, Keisha was tired. And she hadn't found any information on sonar.

The next day, Keisha told her teacher that she had not written her report. She told him there was nothing in the book about it. The teacher opened the book to the index and found *sonar* listed on page 320.

WHAT HAPPENED?

The information Keisha needed was in the book. But Keisha did not know how to find it. She got a zero on her science report because she did not know how to use her textbook. The table of contents and the index would have been especially helpful for finding topics covered in the book.

WHAT DO YOU THINK?

1. What does Keisha need to learn about finding information in books?

2. What parts of a book do you use most when you need to find information?

3. How do you think knowing how to use the parts of a book could help you do your homework easier and faster?

4. How do you think a road map and the index of a book are the same?

KNOWING THE PARTS OF A BOOK

A book has many parts that can give you information. Some of these are

> **At the front of the book**
>
> 1. **Title page:** lists title, **author, publisher,** and place of publication.
> 2. **Copyright page:** tells when the book was published.
> 3. **Table of contents:** lists the chapter headings in the book.
>
> **At the back of the book**
>
> 1. **Bibliography:** lists other books and articles for more information.
> 2. **Index:** a detailed list of topics covered in the book in alphabetical order. It tells the page(s) where the information can be found.
> 3. **Appendix:** has information that does not fit in the body of the book.
> 4. **Glossary:** lists vocabulary words and their meanings as used in that book.

TRY IT OUT!

Tell where you would look for each kind of information. Write the name of the part of the book on the line.

1. the meaning of a vocabulary word as used in that book: _____

2. a subject mentioned in the book: _____

3. the year the book was published: _____

4. the publisher of the book: _____

5. the main topics covered in the book: _____

6. information that does not fit in the text: _____

 Remember, you can get more out of a book if you know how to use its parts.

USING THE TABLE OF CONTENTS

At the front of a textbook, you will find the table of contents. The table of contents lists the names of the chapters you will be reading. It also gives the pages where each chapter can be found.

TRY IT OUT!

Look at the part of a table of contents below. Use it to answer the questions.

Life in America Before the Civil War: 1820–1860		
Chapter 1	**Literature,** Art, and Science	5
Chapter 2	**Education** and Schools	23
Chapter 3	The **Antislavery** Movement	48
Chapter 4	The Women's Rights Movement	61

Write the number of the chapter where each topic could be found:

1. the writer Edgar Allan Poe

2. Horace Mann, a founder of the public school system

3. Susan B. Anthony, women's rights worker

4. how the Underground Railroad helped slaves

5. women's right to vote

6. Frederick Douglass, escaped slave

7. the Hudson River School of painters

8. Maria Mitchell, **astronomer**

9. problems in American schools

10. the first free school for deaf children

11. Harriet Tubman's escape from slavery

 Remember, the table of contents lists chapter names and main topics.

USING THE INDEX

At the end of a textbook, you will find the index. The index lists most topics in the book. It gives the pages on which the topics are found. An index is in alphabetical order.

TRY IT OUT!

Look at part of an index below. Use it to answer the questions.

Middle Ages, 54–57
   rise of trade, 58–59
Middle Colonies, 167–175
   agriculture, 167
   business, 168
   cities, 169
   education, 170
   geography, 171
   religion, 172
   social life, 173

Middle East, 686–687
Midnight judges, 359
Minutemen, 198–199
Missions, Spanish, 64–65
Mississippi River
   in Civil War, 482–483
   exploration of, 102–104
   French control of, 125
   as transportation, 501
   uses, 599

Write the page(s) where each topic could be found:

1. French control of the Mississippi River _____

2. **agriculture** in the Middle Colonies _____

3. rise of trade in the Middle Ages _____

4. Spanish missions _____

5. uses of the Mississippi River _____

6. the Middle East _____

7. the Minutemen _____

8. **religion** in the Middle Colonies _____

9. midnight judges _____

 Remember, an index gives the pages where topics in the book are found.

4 # READING A BAR GRAPH

Visual aids include graphs, charts, and pictures. Visual aids give information in a way that you can see. This may give you a better concept of the main idea of the information. Sometimes the information in the visual aid is not given in the text.

A **bar graph** is one kind of visual aid. The bar graph below has a number line on the bottom. The length of each bar shows how many miles per hour an animal can run.

TRY IT OUT!

Look at the bar graph. Answer the questions that follow it.

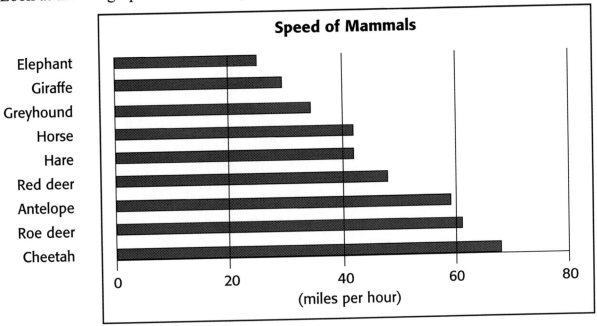

1. What do the bars stand for on this graph?

2. Name two mammals that can run faster than 50 miles per hour.

    a.   b.

3. Why do you think it is important to read graphs in a textbook?

 Remember, visual aids often give information not found in the text.

5 READING A PIE CHART

A **pie chart** looks like a pie divided into slices. The title of the chart shows the subject of the whole chart. Each "slice" of the "pie" stands for part of the whole. All the parts add up to 100%. Very small parts are combined and shown as "other."

TRY IT OUT!

Look at the pie chart. Answer the questions that follow it.

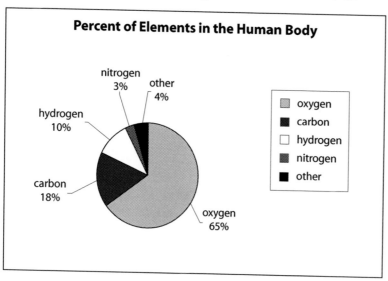

1. What is this chart about?

2. What do the slices of the pie stand for?

3. Which **element** makes up the largest percent of the body?

4. Why do you think there is a slice called "other"?

5. You could read a list of elements in the body in your book. Or you could study the pie chart. Both have the same information. But which way is easier for you to understand? Explain your answer.

 Remember, a pie chart shows the relationship of parts to the whole.

6 GETTING INFORMATION FROM BOOKS AT SCHOOL

Many textbooks have a glossary in the back. A glossary lists key vocabulary words in the book. A glossary is different from a dictionary because it gives the meanings of the words only as they are used in that book. A dictionary, on the other hand, may give a number of meanings for the same word.

TRY IT OUT!

Look at part of a glossary from a science book and part of a dictionary below. Use them to answer the questions.

Glossary	**Dictionary**
charge physical property of matter that can give rise to an electric force of attraction or repulsion	**charge** (chärj) (*verb*) 1. to price 2. to demand payment 3. to attack violently 4. to accuse, blame 5. to command, order 6. to entrust with a duty 7. to fill, load 8. to energize (*noun*) 1. an amount asked as payment 2. care, control 3. a person for whom one is responsible 4. a task 5. an accusation 6. an attack 7. the amount of electrical charge in an object 8. an explosive

1. What information is found in the glossary definition of *charge?*

2. Name two ways the dictionary entry for *charge* is different from the glossary entry.

    a.

    b.

3. You are told to look up a list of 20 science words. You will be tested on the definitions. Would you use the glossary or the dictionary? Explain your answer.

4. Why might it be more difficult to find the correct meaning for a science word as used in your textbook in the dictionary than in the glossary?

7 GETTING INFORMATION FROM BOOKS AT HOME

Terrence wanted to buy a cell phone. He had seen many ads on television and in the newspaper. Each company said they had the best deal.

In a magazine, Terrence found an article comparing three cell-phone companies. The information he needed was in a chart.

TRY IT OUT!

Look at the chart. Answer the questions that follow.

	Telright	Easyphone	Phonecheap
Monthly fee	$39.95	$45.00	$29.95
Minutes included			
Mon.–Fri. 6 A.M.–9 P.M.	300	600	100
Other times	100	600	100
Extra minutes	$.35/minute	$.20/minute	$.55/minute
Long-distance minutes	No additional charge	No additional charge	$.75/minute
Directory assistance	$2.00/call	free	$1.50/call
Contract terms			
Length	1 year	1 year	none
Early-termination fee	$175	$250	none
Start-up fee	$35	$50	$35

1. What is this chart about?

2. Which two plans have no additional charge for long-distance calls?

3. Which two plans have a one-year contract?

(continued)

7 **GETTING INFORMATION FROM BOOKS AT HOME** *(continued)*

4. The early-termination fee is charged if you break (**terminate**) the contract before the year is up. Which plan has no termination fee?

5. Which plan includes the most daytime minutes?

6. Which plan is cheapest if you use the phone only once in a while for **emergencies?**

7. Which plan is best if you make a lot of long-distance calls?

8. Which plan has free directory assistance?

9. Which plan costs the most for extra minutes?

10. If you were getting a cell phone, which phone would be best for you? Explain your answer.

11. Why do you think having a cell phone would be useful?

12. How could you find the best deal on a cell phone today?

GETTING INFORMATION FROM BOOKS AT WORK

 Doug had a new job at the hospital. When he was hired, he was given a copy of the Employee Handbook. When he had a question about company rules, this book usually had the answer.

TRY IT OUT!

Use the index that follows to answer the questions below.

Back Safety Training, 45

Campus Police, 35

Conduct, 32

Death in Employee's Family, 9

Educational Leave, 14

Exit Interview, 8

Family and Medical Leave, 34

Firearms Policy, 2

Harassment Policy, 12

Holidays, 32

Hours of Work, 24

ID badges, 5

Inclement Weather Policy, 25

Insurance Policies, 18

Lost and Found, 17

Lunch Break, 16

Major Medical Leave, 22

Military Leave, 14

Overtime, 23

Parking, 19

Pay and Raises, 14

Personal Leave, 34

Resignation, 36

Rest Breaks, 16

Sick Leave, 34

Smoking, 10

Voting, 6

1. What do you think is the purpose of an employee handbook?

2. Why would it be important for a new employee to read the handbook?

3. Why would it be a good idea to keep the handbook on hand?

4. On which page would Doug find the answer to each of these questions:
   a. When do I eat lunch? _____
   b. Do I get the day off on Valentine's Day? _____
   c. Should I have any rest breaks? _____
   d. What hours should I be at work? _____
   e. Where do I turn in a jacket I found in the parking lot? _____
   f. Is it OK to take a college class during work hours? _____
   g. What do I do if I get sick? _____
   h. Will I get paid extra for overtime? _____
   i. Where do I park? _____
   j. How can I get a raise? _____

USING YOUR LEARNING STYLE TO GET INFORMATION FROM BOOKS

Visual learners

Visual learners may scan the table of contents to get an overview of the contents of a book. They can look for visual aids in their books and read definitions in the glossary.

Auditory learners

Auditory learners may discuss the table of contents and decide on the main ideas of a book. Auditory learners may discuss the meaning of visual aids. They may form study groups to learn definitions found in the glossary.

Kinesthetic learners

Kinesthetic learners may make a chart showing the main ideas of a book. They may make their own visual aids to help them learn main ideas. They may type a list of definitions to learn.

Write your learning style here: _____

(visual, auditory, or kinesthetic)

Now answer each question below.

1. A history test will cover information shown in a pie chart in the book. How do you think you should use your learning style to study the chart?

2. You looked up a topic in the index, but you couldn't find it. You know the topic is covered somewhere in the book. How do you think you could use your learning style to help you find it?

3. How do you think you should use your learning style to study a list of words you looked up in the glossary?

⑩ CHAPTER TEST

Write **True** or **False** on the line by each statement. If the sentence is false, explain why it is false in the space below the sentence.

_____ 1. Knowing how to use the parts of a book can help you do your homework.

_____ 2. The author of the book is listed on the copyright page.

_____ 3. The title page lists only the title of the book.

_____ 4. The bibliography is an alphabetical listing of topics in the book.

_____ 5. The table of contents lists chapter headings in the book.

_____ 6. A glossary is the same as a dictionary.

_____ 7. To find out when the book was published, look on the title page.

_____ 8. The appendix has information that does not fit in the body of the book.

_____ 9. If a book has a table of contents, it rarely has an index.

_____ 10. The glossary only gives the meaning of the word as it is used in the book.

(continued)

10 CHAPTER TEST *(continued)*

_____ 11. Visual aids are photographs.

_____ 12. Bar graphs and pie charts are two examples of visual aids.

_____ 13. Each slice on a pie graph shows how much of the whole it stands for.

_____ 14. On a pie graph, very small parts can be shown together as "other."

_____ 15. All the parts of a pie graph add up to 100%.

_____ 16. A dictionary may give many meanings for the same word.

_____ 17. A dictionary is the best place to look up a list of math terms.

_____ 18. It could be harder to find the exact meaning of a math term in the dictionary than in the glossary.

_____ 19. The bibliography tells where the author of the book got information.

_____ 20. The index lists terms in order by chapters.

CHAPTER 5: UNDERSTANDING WHAT YOU READ

Terrell had to read a lot. At school, he had to read his textbooks. He had to read information on the Internet to do reports. At home, he had to read the newspaper to get sports scores. He had to read the television schedule. At work, Terrell had to read directions. He had to read his employee handbook.

But Terrell did not like to read. His mind wandered. He lost his place. He found himself reading the same thing over and over. He was never quite sure what he had read. After he was done reading, Terrell usually forgot most of what he had read. Terrell wished reading was easier for him.

WHAT HAPPENED?

Terrell knew how to read. That is, he knew how to read words. But he didn't know how to read for understanding. Terrell's eyes moved across the page. But he was not actively reading for understanding.

WHAT DO YOU THINK?

1. What kinds of things did Terrell have to read at home and at work?

2. What problems did Terrell have as he read?

3. What are some things you read at home or at work other than school assignments?

4. What do you think are your weak points in reading?

5. Do you think it would help you if you understood more of what you read? Explain your answer.

BEING AN ACTIVE READER

A good way to understand what you read is to use the **Active** Reading system:

1. **SCAN** the material to get the main idea quickly. Read the title. Look at the headings. Look at the words in **bold** or *italic* print. Look at the visual aids (pictures, charts, and graphs). Read the summary. You should have the main idea of what the material is about.

2. **READ** the material. Each time you come to a heading, stop! Turn the heading into a question. Try to answer your question when you're finished reading. This will give you a purpose for your reading.

3. **REVIEW** the material. After you've finished reading, you are not done! Go back and scan the material again. This review will help you keep the material in your brain. State the main idea of the material under each heading.

WHAT DO YOU THINK?

1. What is the purpose of scanning material before you read it?

2. Why do you think turning each heading into a question gives you a purpose for your reading?

3. Why do you think you should review the material after you have read it?

 Remember, the three steps to Active Reading are scan, read, and review.

2 ACTIVE READING STEP 1: SCAN

Scan the article below. Then answer the questions.

JACQUES COUSTEAU

HE LEARNED TO LOVE THE SEA

Jacques Cousteau was born in France in 1910. His first love was flying. At the age of 26, he was learning to fly for the French Navy. An accident damaged his arm. He could no longer fly. He was sent to the beach to get well. While there, he began diving to watch fish. He later wrote his "eyes were opened to the world beneath the surface of the sea."

INVENTOR AND SPY

During World War II, Cousteau became a spy. He helped the **Allies** win the war. He kept diving. He learned underwater photography. He invented the **Aqua-Lung,** the first **scuba** equipment.

MOVIE MAKER

After the war, Cousteau made films about life in the sea. His movie *The Silent World* showed the beauty of life under the sea. It also showed the adventure of diving. Scuba diving became popular.

THE *CALYPSO*

Cousteau continued to roam the world in his research ship the *Calypso.* He made over 100 films. He talked about **pollution,** oil spills, and overfishing. He worked to protect the oceans for the future.

---

1. What is the title of the article?

2. List the vocabulary words found in bold print. You should know what each word means.

3. What do you think the main idea of the article will be?

 Remember, scanning gives you the main idea of the material.

ACTIVE READING STEP 2: READ

Reading with a purpose can help you **focus** on what you are reading. To give your reading a purpose, turn each heading into a question. For example, in the story on page 64, you could turn the heading **"The Calypso"** into the question "What is the *Calypso*?" Keep your question in mind as you read. When you finish the section, you should be able to answer it.

As you read, pay attention to all words in bold type. Ask yourself why the word is important. You should know when you finish the section. You should also be able to answer any review questions at the end of the section.

Answer the questions that follow by looking back at the article on page 64. Then read the article.

1. Write a question for each heading:

   a. He Learned to Love the Sea

   b. Inventor and Spy

   c. Movie Maker

   d. The *Calypso*

2. List the words in bold print. Tell what each means. Use the dictionary if you need to.

   a.

   b.

   c.

   d.

 Remember, turn each heading into a question as you read.

ACTIVE READING STEP 3: REVIEW

You scanned the material. You read it. But don't shut that book! There is one more step to good reading. Taking just a few minutes to review what you've read will really make it stick in your brain!

Here's how to review:

1. Go back to the beginning of the material.
2. Scan it like you did the first time. Read each heading. State what was in that section in your own words.
3. Look at each word in bold print. Tell what it means.

WHAT DO YOU THINK?

1. Why do you think many students skip the "Review" step when reading?

2. What do you think is the reason to scan the material a second time to review?

3. Why do you think it is important to state what is in each section in your own words?

4. Why do you think it is important to know what each word in bold print means?

 Remember, reviewing after you read will help you remember better.

5 UNDERSTANDING WHAT YOU READ AT SCHOOL

Read the section below. Then answer the questions that follow it.

CIVIL WAR AMENDMENTS

Three **amendments** to the U.S. Constitution were passed after the Civil War. The first outlawed slavery. The other two gave the rights of the Constitution to African Americans.

THE THIRTEENTH AMENDMENT (1865)

This amendment ended slavery in the United States. It freed thousands of African Americans. It made forced labor against the law (except as punishment for a crime).

THE FOURTEENTH AMENDMENT (1868)

This amendment defined a U.S. **citizen** as anyone born in the United States. This meant most African Americans were citizens for the first time. The amendment also required every state to give its citizens "equal protection of the laws." This meant that state governments had to treat all their citizens equally.

THE FIFTEENTH AMENDMENT (1870)

This amendment gave African Americans **suffrage,** the right to vote. This right was given only to men. Women of any race did not get the right to vote until 1920.

1. What is this selection about?

2. Which amendment freed the slaves?

3. Which amendment gave African-American men the right to vote?

4. Which amendment made African Americans citizens?

5. Put an X on the line in front of each person who could vote in 1868.

_____ a white man   _____ a black man   _____ a white woman

_____ a black woman   _____ a Native-American woman

6 UNDERSTANDING WHAT YOU READ AT HOME

There are many uses for Active Reading at home. Read the **warranty** on goods before you buy. Know how long the warranty is good for. Learn what it covers.

Read the warranty on a DVD player. Answer the questions that follow.

Warranty

Length of warranty. This product is covered against **defects** in materials and workmanship for a period of one year from date of **purchase.**

What is covered. We will repair or replace this product at our **option** and at no charge during the warranty period. The product must be returned to our service center. The warranty covers defects in materials and workmanship found in normal use of the product. It does not cover damage caused by misuse, fire, water, electrical problems, or damage caused by incorrect **installation.** To receive warranty service, the original dated receipt must be shown as proof of purchase. The warranty is **valid** only on products purchased and used in the United States. It does not include transportation, installation, removal, or reinstallation.

1. If the product is covered by the warranty, write **Yes** on the line. If not, write **No.** Explain each answer.

   _____ a. You bought the DVD player on sale. It stops working six months later.

   _____ b. You hooked up the DVD player wrong, and it stops working.

   _____ c. You purchased the DVD player in Canada. It stops working one month after purchase.

   _____ d. You bought the DVD player in October. But you didn't open the box until December. In November of the next year, the player broke.

   _____ e. You spilled water on the DVD player. It stopped working.

2. How much does it cost to have the product repaired if it is under warranty?

7 UNDERSTANDING WHAT YOU READ AT WORK

Read the information for new employees. Answer the questions that follow.

Initial Employment Period

All new **employees** are in the **initial employment period** for the first 90 days of employment. During this period, the **employer** will watch the employee's work closely. If there are problems, the employee will be given time to improve. Problems will be explained to the employee in writing. At the end of 90 days, the employee will be **evaluated.** A new employee can be **terminated** at any time during the 90-day period if work is not satisfactory.

A new employee will earn **personal days** and **sick days** during the initial employment period. However, he/she may not use this leave during the initial employment period. Any time off during this period will be unpaid leave.

1. What do you think is the purpose of the initial employment period?

2. What will happen if a new employee needs to take a personal day during the initial employment period?

3. What will happen if a new employee does not do satisfactory work?

4. If a new employee does good work, what will happen at the end of the 90 days?

5. How much will a new employee be paid for the two days he or she calls in sick?

6. Why do you think it would be important to read and understand the material in this section of the employee handbook?

USING YOUR LEARNING STYLE TO UNDERSTAND WHAT YOU READ

You can use your learning style to help you understand what you read. Here are a few suggestions:

Visual learner

Visual learners might make a study guide using the questions they made from each heading in the chapter. They might make a list of all words in bold print and their definitions.

Auditory learner

Auditory learners might quiz themselves out loud on the questions made from each heading in the chapter. They might tape-record the questions and answer them. They might make a list of all words in bold print and study them out loud with a friend.

Kinesthetic learner

A kinesthetic learner might make a chart listing the steps in Active Reading. They might act out the steps in Active Reading for the class. They could make a poster listing the steps in Active Reading.

Write your learning style here: _____
                                    (visual, auditory, or kinesthetic)
Now answer each question below.

1. When scanning, you look over the chapter before you read it. How could you use your learning style to help you get more out of scanning?

2. When reading a chapter, you turn headings into questions. How might you use your learning style to help you do this?

3. How do you think you could use your learning style to help you review a chapter after reading it?

9 CHAPTER TEST

1. Name the three steps in Active Reading.

    a.   b.   c.

2. Explain the purpose of scanning material before you read.

3. What is the purpose of turning headings into questions as you read?

4. What is the purpose of reviewing after you have finished reading?

5. What should you do when you see a word in bold print or italics?

6. Why do you think Active Reading can help you get more out of your reading?

7. List four things you should look at when you scan a selection.

    a.

    b.

    c.

    d.

CHAPTER 6: LEARNING TO TAKE NOTES

Pat was in art class. Her teacher was talking to the class about modern art. Pat knew material from class would be on the test. She wrote down every word the teacher said. Later, she couldn't make any sense out of her notes.

José was in the same class. He thought taking notes was a waste of time. He was sure he could remember without taking notes.

Jamal was in art class, too. He wasn't thinking about art. He watched some girls outside the window. He wrote his friend a letter. Once in a while, he took a few notes.

WHAT HAPPENED?

All three students knew the test would include material presented in class. All three thought they were doing what they should to be ready for the test. But none of them was. Pat was taking too many notes. She was not listening to the meaning of what was being said. José wasn't bothering with taking any notes. And Jamal was paying little attention to the teacher.

WHAT DO YOU THINK?

1. Why do you think Pat did not have good notes?

2. Why do you think José did not have good notes?

3. Why do you think Jamal did not have good notes?

4. Why do you think it is important to have good classroom notes?

5. How would you rate your own note-taking skills?

1 BEING AN ACTIVE LISTENER

> Pete was in the den. The news was on television. Pete was fixing a snack and talking to a friend on the phone. He heard the news, but he wasn't paying much attention.
>
> Then the sports announcer came on. He began to tell about a football game played last night by Pete's favorite team. Suddenly, Pete was all ears. He sat down and listened carefully to every word. He wanted to be able to talk about the game with his friend later.

In this story, Pete started as a **passive** listener. He heard the news, but he wasn't really listening to it. When the football story came on, Pete became an **active** listener. He was no longer just hearing the words. He was thinking about and trying to understand what was being said.

WHAT DO YOU THINK?

1. What do you think is the difference between passive and active listening?

2. Give an example of a time when you were a passive listener.

3. Give an example of a time when you were an active listener.

4. Why do you think an active listener will take better notes?

 Remember, active listeners hear and try to understand what is being said.

2 TAKING GOOD NOTES

Here are seven tips for taking notes. Read them and answer the questions that follow.

1. Be an active listener. Think about what the teacher is saying. If you don't understand something, ask questions.
2. Don't get **distracted.** Avoid daydreaming, talking, or looking out the window.
3. Take notes that are neat and easy to read. Use a pencil so you can erase.
4. Write down anything the teacher writes on the board or on the overhead.
5. Listen for clues that the teacher is about to say something important. (Examples: "The main idea is . . ." or "There are three main reasons that . . .")
6. Read over your notes. Rewrite them if they are not clear. Do this as soon as you can after class.
7. If you are absent, get notes from someone else.

WHAT DO YOU THINK?

1. What should you do if you don't understand something the teacher says?

2. Why do you think you should write down everything the teacher writes on the board?

3. Write a clue teachers might give when they are about to say something important.

4. Why is it a good idea to read over your notes after class? Why should you rewrite unclear notes?

 Remember, taking notes will help you remember what you hear.

3 FOLLOWING THE CLUES TO TAKE GOOD NOTES

What do an alarm clock, a siren, and a person yelling "Fire!" have in common? Each is a way to get your attention. Teachers also have ways to get your attention. (Usually they are a lot quieter than the ways listed above.)

Teachers use clues to point out important points. The clues tell you when to be alert. They tell you to write down what you hear next. Here are some of these clues. There are many others.

"Listen to what I am saying."   "In conclusion…"
"Don't forget…"   "The main point is…"
"For this reason…"   "First … second … third …"
"There are three main reasons that…"

WHAT DO YOU THINK?

1. Why do you think numbers can be important clues?

2. List two clues that one of your own teachers uses to alert the class to important points.

   a.

   b.

3. How do you think being aware of a certain teacher's clues could make it easier for you to take notes in that class?

4. You can't write down everything a teacher says. How do you think using clues could help?

5. These same clues are used in textbooks as well as in teachers' lectures. Name some clues you have seen in one of your textbooks.

 Remember, following the clues will help you take more complete notes.

4 USING ABBREVIATIONS AND SYMBOLS IN YOUR NOTES

Using **abbreviations** and **symbols** can help you take notes faster. We use abbreviations every day. You may write 80% instead of 80 percent. You write $5.25 instead of five dollars and twenty-five cents.

You can also make up your own abbreviations. For example, when taking notes on *Tyrannosaurus rex,* you could write *Tyr, TR,* or *T Rex* for *Tyrannosaurus rex.*

The chart below shows other abbreviations and symbols you might want to try.

=	equal, same	>	greater than	<	less than
#	number	↑	increasing, up	↓	decreasing, down
≠	not equal	→	causing	*	most important
eg	for example	b/c	because	esp	especially
w/	with	w/o	without	∴	therefore

TRY IT OUT!

1. Make up abbreviations you could use for the following words:

   a. literature

   c. New York City

   b. part-time job

2. Rewrite the following phrases using abbreviations and/or symbols.

   a. the temperature is rising

   b. cereal with raisins

   c. war without honor

   d. price does not equal quality

 Remember, using abbreviations and symbols will help you take notes faster.

REVIEWING AND REWRITING YOUR NOTES

What should you do with your notes after you take them? As soon as possible, go over your notes. That way, the information is still fresh in your mind. If anything is unclear, correct it. Add any information you need to make your notes clear. Ask your teacher or a friend if you need help.

You should rewrite your notes if they are hard to read. Use your own words when you rewrite. Write out abbreviations and symbols if that makes things more clear to you.

If you do this, you will have better notes. But most importantly, you will be learning the material as you rewrite. This takes a little time. But it will pay off when it is time for the test. You will find that you have better notes to study from.

TRY IT OUT!

Martha took the following sets of notes. Later, a good friend who had been absent asked to copy the notes. Martha decided to rewrite the notes for her friend, leaving out the symbols and abbreviations. Rewrite the notes using no symbols or abbreviations.

The Giant Panda

> G.P. endangered < 1,000 in wild.
> Adult > 6 ft. tall and > 220 lbs.
> At birth G.P. < rat
> G. P. * food bamboo.

 Remember, go over your notes as soon as you can after you take them and rewrite them if needed.

6 TAKING NOTES AT SCHOOL

Taking notes at school can make all the difference in your grades. Below, you will find a lecture given by a history teacher. Take notes on it. Use abbreviations and symbols in your notes.

Stories of lost lands have interested scientists for years. One of the most important **legends** that turned out to be true is the story of Troy. The ancient poet Homer wrote of a war between the Greeks and Trojans. The war lasted more than 10 years. The Greeks could not break down the walls of Troy.

First, the Greeks made a huge wooden horse and brought it to the front gate of Troy. They said it was a peace offering. Second, the Trojans pulled the horse inside the city of Troy. Inside the horse were hundreds of Greek warriors. The important part came when night fell. The Greeks climbed out of the horse, attacked the sleeping city, and ended the war.

For years, the world thought that Homer made up the story. But in 1873, a German **archaeologist,** Heinrich Schliemann, announced he had found the ruins of Troy in what is now Turkey. Since then, it has been proven that the ruins were Troy, a city that fell more than 5,000 years ago.

7 TAKING NOTES AT HOME

There will be many times you need to take notes on information you get at home. Read each story below. Write notes on the directions given to Kathy and Sue in the spaces below the stories. Try to use abbreviations and symbols.

1. Kathy had a tree in her yard. A storm broke off three main limbs. She called a garden store to find out what to do. The man said, "First, saw off each broken limb. Cut below where it is broken. Paint roof tar on the cut place. Or we sell Prune-Stop you can use. Put more than two coats on. That will keep bugs from eating into the tree."

2. Sue wanted to open a checking account. She went to three banks and asked the same questions. Here is what the banker at the first bank told Sue: "The minimum deposit to open an account is $25. We do not pay interest. There will be a fee of three dollars if your balance falls below $25. There is a fee of 20¢ for each check you write. You get a free ATM card good at all of our branch banks."

3. Why do you think taking notes could help you remember all the information?

79

8 TAKING NOTES AT WORK

Larry got a job with a **landscaping** company. He liked his job because he liked to be outdoors. Larry wanted to be sure he did each job right. So he took notes on the directions he was given for each job.

Take notes on the instructions below. Use abbreviations and symbols.

1. Planting **shrubs:** The best time to plant shrubs is in late winter or early spring. Dig a planting hole about twice the width and twice the depth of the rootball. Put the shrub in the hole. **Tamp** the soil around the roots. Water well. Cover the soil around the shrub with **mulch.** You can use peat moss or pine bark as mulch. Apply a layer of mulch 2–3 inches thick. Water the shrub regularly. Water thoroughly, but don't overwater. Let the soil dry out a little before watering again.

2. Why do you think taking notes could help you do better at work?

3. Where do you think you might keep the notes you take at work?

  walch.com © 2003 Walch Publishing

USING YOUR LEARNING STYLE TO TAKE NOTES

You can use your learning style to help you take better notes. Here are a few suggestions:

Visual learner

Visual learners should spend extra time going over notes at home. They might compare them to the textbook or manual to see if all important points are included. They should highlight important points in their notes. They may wish to rewrite them into paragraph or outline form.

Auditory learner

Auditory learners may like going over their notes with a friend. They may like to listen carefully to the sound of the teacher's or employer's voice to detect clues about important points. Auditory learners may use their notes in a study group.

Kinesthetic learner

Kinesthetic learners may wish to draw pictures of important points in their notes. They may like to watch the teacher or employer for body language that shows an important point being stressed. Kinesthetic learners may like to rewrite and illustrate their notes.

Write your learning style here: _____

(visual, auditory, or kinesthetic)

Now answer each question below.

1. How do you think you can use your learning style to help you take better notes in class or at work?

2. How do you think you could use your learning style to review your notes?

3. How do you think you could use your learning style to use your notes to study for a test?

🔟 CHAPTER TEST

1. Explain the difference between an active and a passive listener.

2. Give two examples of clues teachers give to show that they are about to say something you should write down.

    a.

    b.

3. Why is it a good idea to read over your notes as soon as possible after class?

4. Write symbols or abbreviations for the following:
    a. decreasing
    b. because
    c. especially
    d. most importantly
    e. without

5. Why do you think you should write down what the teacher writes on the board or on the overhead?

6. Why is it a good idea to take notes in pencil?

7. Why are numbers an important clue that something important is about to follow?

8. Name two distractions that would keep you from taking good notes in class.

    a.

    b.

CHAPTER 7: REMEMBERING WHAT YOU LEARN

Paul knew all the words to his favorite songs on the radio. But he thought he couldn't **memorize** a poem for English.

Mary listened to the teacher. She didn't remember most of what was said.

Matt looked over his math notes the night before the test. On the test, he didn't remember the formulas.

Alice did not understand geometry. She tried to just memorize the definitions.

Tim had a lot of vocabulary words to learn. He sat for hours going over them. It didn't seem like he was remembering them very well.

WHAT HAPPENED?

These students did not know how to remember what they learned. Here are some important rules about how memory works:

1. It is easier to remember things you *want* to remember. (Paul wanted to learn those songs. His teacher wanted him to learn the poem.)
2. It is easier to learn when you are *actively* involved by taking notes, reading aloud, or discussing material. (Mary sat passively in class. She hoped to soak up the material just by sitting there.)
3. Reviewing material over and over is the best way to learn. (Matt hoped to learn his math formulas by going over them once.)
4. It is much easier to learn something that makes sense. (Alice was trying to memorize definitions that made no sense to her.)
5. You will remember more by studying in several short sessions than one long session. (Tim tried to study for hours at a time. Several shorter times would work better.)

WHAT DO YOU THINK?

1. Why do you think you might learn something you really *want* to learn more easily than something that doesn't interest you?

2. Why do you think it is easier to learn something that makes sense?

3. Why do you think you will remember more from several short sessions than from one long one?

REMEMBERING VOCABULARY WORDS

There will be many times at school, home, and work when you need to learn and remember new **vocabulary** words. Here's how to make this job easier:

1. Be sure you know what the word means. Look it up in the glossary or dictionary. Read the definition. Make sure you understand it.
2. Write the definition in your own words. Writing it down helps it stick in your mind.
3. Review the word often. Flash cards are a good way to review.
4. Think of clues to help you remember the word.

WHAT DO YOU THINK?

Write **True** or **False** by each sentence below. If the sentence is false, tell why.

_____ 1. Looking for clues to help you remember the meaning of a word is a waste of time.

_____ 2. The best way to remember a list of new words is to review them often.

_____ 3. If you have many words to learn, writing each one on a flash card and reviewing them often helps you remember them.

_____ 4. Memorizing a dictionary definition word for word is the best way to remember the meaning of a word.

> **Remember, make sure you understand the meaning of a new word, then review it often to learn it.**

REMEMBERING WHAT YOU READ

Remember the Active Reading system from Chapter 5? You will use this system again to help you remember what you read.

First, scan the entire selection quickly. Then go back and read a short section of the material. Turn headings into questions. Write the answers to the questions in your notes. Also write in your notes the meanings of any words in bold or italic print. Be sure to use your own words.

Taking notes makes reading an active process. You have to pay attention and think about what you're reading. You scan, read, write notes, and review. You have actually gone over the same material three different ways. No wonder you're more likely to remember it!

WHAT DO YOU THINK?

1. Why do you think you should write down the answer to each of the questions you made up from the headings?

2. Why do you think you should write the meanings of words in bold or italic print in your notes?

3. Why do you think it is important not to copy your notes right out of the book?

4. Why do you think taking notes helps you remember better?

 Remember, taking notes will help you remember what you read.

3 REMEMBERING LONGER PASSAGES

Sometimes you may need to memorize a longer **passage** word for word. This is a big job. The secret is to take it one step at a time.

1. Read the entire passage.
2. Look up any words you don't know. Write their definitions in your own words.
3. Break the passage into parts. A part might be one sentence or a group of sentences that express a thought.
4. Memorize the first part.
5. Once you've learned that, add the second part. Repeat until you can say the two parts together.
6. Keep adding parts to what you've learned.
7. Once you've learned the whole thing, review it often.

TRY IT OUT!

Put an X in front of each statement below that shows a good way to memorize a long poem.

_____ 1. Before you start to memorize, read through the whole poem.

_____ 2. Look up each word in the poem that you don't know.

_____ 3. Don't worry about what the poem means. That won't help you learn it.

_____ 4. Break the poem into parts.

_____ 5. Learn the first part. Then add one more part. Keep on adding parts until you have learned the whole poem.

_____ 6. Learn the sentences of the poem in any order you want. Later you can put them into the correct order.

_____ 7. When you have learned the whole poem, practice it over and over.

_____ 8. Set aside an hour the night before you are to know the poem. Don't look at the poem before then.

_____ 9. Once you can say the whole thing, you don't need to practice any more.

 Remember, to memorize a longer passage, break it into parts and learn one part at a time.

4 REMEMBERING USING REPETITION AND MIND PICTURES

Repetition means reading, writing, and saying information a number of times. First read the information. Then cover it and try to write it from memory. Say the information from memory. Repeat several times.

1. Try to remember the following facts using repetition. Once you've learned them, say them aloud or write them without looking.

   a. The three branches of government are the legislative, executive, and judicial.

   b. The capital of Wyoming is Cheyenne. The capital of Montana is Helena. The capital of Delaware is Dover.

Using **mind pictures** means making a picture in your mind that helps you remember. Read the information. Then think of a picture that shows the information. See the picture in your mind as you say the information out loud.

2. Describe a mind picture you could use to remember each of the following:

   a. American colonists defied the British in an act called The Boston Tea Party in 1773.

   b. Many American ships were sunk in the Japanese bombing of Pearl Harbor in 1941.

 Remember, using repetition and mind pictures can help you remember.

REMEMBERING USING GROUPING AND RHYMING

Grouping means putting facts into groups that make sense. Practice the facts by groups. You may wish to name each group.

1. Read List I three times. Then turn the paper over. Write as much of the list as you can remember on the back of this page. Next, read List II three times. Turn the paper over. Write as much of List II as you can.

I.

dishwasher
apples
mixer
crackers
microwave
bread

II.

apples
bread
crackers
_____
dishwasher
microwave
mixer

2. Which list was easier to remember and why?

Rhyming means thinking of rhymes that help you remember a fact. For example, "In 1492, Columbus sailed the ocean blue."

3. Make up a rhyme to help you remember each fact below.

   a. The Wright brothers flew the first airplane in 1903.

   b. The Model T was built in the first assembly line.

 Remember, put facts into groups or think of rhymes to help you remember.

6 REMEMBERING USING ACRONYMS AND ASSOCIATION

Acronyms are words formed by the first letters of the words to be remembered. For example, many students remember the names of the Great Lakes by the acronym HOMES (Huron, Ontario, Michigan, Erie, and Superior).

To make an acronym, write the facts you want to remember. Underline the first letter in each fact. Arrange the underlined letters to make a word.

1. Make up an acronym to help you remember each fact below. You may use the underlined letter to help you.

   a. Three common trees in the south are the pine, the magnolia, and the oak.

   b. Thomas Edison invented the lightbulb, movie projector, and alkaline battery.

Association means tying (associating) a fact you want to learn to one you already know. For example, "The inventor of the telephone was Alexander Graham Bell." You might associate *bell* with a telephone ringing. Or you might think of Bell Telephone Company.

2. Try to write an association you could use to remember each fact.

   a. Dr. Rudolph Diesel, a German engineer, invented the diesel engine.

   b. Raymond Kuhl invented one of the first snowmobiles.

 Remember, use acronyms and association to help you remember.

7 REMEMBERING AT SCHOOL

1. Make up a rhyme that could help you remember each fact below.

    a. The word smog is a combination of *fog* and *smoke*.

    b. The year the French and Indian War started was 1754.

2. Make up an acronym that could help you remember each fact below. (You may arrange the letters in any order to form a word.)

    a. Cold-blooded animals include <u>r</u>eptiles, <u>f</u>ish, and <u>a</u>mphibians.

    b. <u>L</u>izards, <u>s</u>nakes, <u>a</u>lligators, and <u>t</u>urtles are examples of reptiles.

3. Think of an association that could help you remember each fact below.

    a. <u>Zoo</u>logy is the study of <u>animals</u>.

    b. The <u>Iron</u> Age was the time in history when people first learned to make <u>tools</u>.

(continued)

walch.com © 2003 Walch Publishing

REMEMBERING AT SCHOOL *(continued)*

4. Write the endangered animals in groups to help you remember them more easily.

key deer
snail darter
California condor
grizzly bear
bull trout
woodland caribou

Chinook salmon
whooping crane
bald eagle
American alligator
American crocodile
ivory-billed woodpecker

Louisiana black bear
Wyoming toad
Kemp's ridley sea turtle
desert pupfish

Mammals	Birds	Reptiles/Amphibians	Fish

5. Once you have grouped the animals, explain how you would learn them.

8 REMEMBERING AT HOME

Mario was looking for an apartment. He read the ads. He found three apartments near his job. He read over the ads. But he couldn't remember all the facts. He couldn't decide which apartment was best.

#1	#2	#3
Furn. 1 bdrm apt. Water inc. $325/mo. Sec. dep. $325. 1 yr lease 555-4583.	Nice unfurn. apt. New. 1 bdrm. $425/mo. Sec. dep. $300. 6 mo. lease. Water inc. 555-4993.	Furn. 2 bdrm apt. All utilities included. $425/mo. Sec. dep. $350. 1 yr. lease 555-4930.

WHAT DO YOU THINK?

1. Mario knew it would be easier to remember something that makes sense. Here are the words from the ads that he did not know. Write the meaning of each word on the line. You may use a dictionary.

   a. **furnished** (furn.)_____

   b. unfurnished (unfurn.)_____

   c. **utilities** _____

   d. **security deposit** (sec. dep.)_____

   e. **lease** _____

2. Mario knew it would be easier to remember things in groups. He organized the facts in the ads so he could compare the apartments. Write the facts for each apartment in the right boxes in the chart below.

	Apartment #1	Apartment #2	Apartment #3
Furnished or unfurnished			
Number of bedrooms			
Amount of rent			
Amount of security deposit			
Utilities included?			
Length of lease			

3. Which apartment do you think Mario should rent? Explain your answer.

9 REMEMBERING AT WORK

Frank had a new job as an assistant to an electrician. Before he could begin work, Frank had to pass a safety test. Frank's boss gave him some material to learn for the test. It was 20 pages long. Frank used his learning strategies to help him remember the information.

WHAT DO YOU THINK?

1. There were many words Frank did not know in the safety information. Put an X by each thing he should do to remember the words.

   _____ a. Make a list of all the words he doesn't know.

   _____ b. Look up the meaning of each word and copy it word for word.

   _____ c. Write the meaning of each word in his own words.

   _____ d. Be sure he understands the meaning of each word.

   _____ e. Make flash cards and review them often.

   _____ f. Don't worry about the meaning of the words. Just try to get the main idea of the material.

   _____ g. Think of clues to help him remember words he has trouble remembering.

   _____ h. Use his learning style to help him remember.

2. Frank knows he must read and remember all the safety rules. Put an X by each thing he should do to help him remember what he reads.

   _____ a. Scan over a section of the material before he begins reading.

   _____ b. Turn headings into questions.

   _____ c. Take notes on the answers to his questions.

   _____ d. Copy the rules word for word. Don't worry about understanding them.

   _____ e. Review his notes often.

   _____ f. Read it once and trust his memory.

   _____ g. Stay up all night trying to memorize the rules.

3. Frank knows it is easier to remember something you *want* to remember. Why do you think Frank really wants to remember the material for the safety test?

⓾ USING YOUR LEARNING STYLE TO REMEMBER WHAT YOU LEARN

You can use your learning style to help you remember what you learn. Here are a few suggestions:

Visual learner

Visual learners should write down things they want to remember and read their notes often. They may write memory aids and read them often. They may want to make flash cards and outlines to review.

Auditory learner

Auditory learners should recite the rhymes, acronyms, and other memory aids they make for themselves out loud. They should review material they want to learn out loud. They may wish to review out loud with a friend.

Kinesthetic learner

Kinesthetic learners may like to draw their memory aids on paper. They may enjoy using mind pictures to help them remember. They may like playing flash card games with a friend.

Write your learning style here: _____

(visual, auditory, or kinesthetic)

Now answer each question below.

1. How do you think you could use your learning style to help you remember a list of vocabulary words?

2. How do you think you could use your learning style to help you memorize a poem?

3. Give an example of a memory aid that you are interested in using. Tell how you would use the memory aid and your learning style to help you study for a test.

11 CHAPTER TEST

1. Write each memory aid from the box on the line next to its definition.

repetition	mind picture	grouping	rhyming	acronym	association

_____ a. formed by the first letters of each word to be remembered

_____ b. tying a fact to be remembered to something already known

_____ c. putting facts to be learned into groups to organize them

_____ d forming an image in your mind to help you remember

_____ e. making up a poem or rhyme

_____ f. reading, writing, or saying information over and over

2. Put an X by each correct way to memorize a long poem.

_____ a. Read through the whole poem over and over until you know it.

_____ b. Look up all words you don't know and copy their definitions exactly.

_____ c. Write definitions of words you don't know in your own words.

_____ d. Break the poem into parts. Learn one part at a time.

_____ e. Once you've learned the poem, review it often.

_____ f. Once you've learned the poem, don't look at it again.

3. Why do you remember better when you take notes in class?

4. Put an X by each correct way to learn a list of 10 new vocabulary words.

_____ a. Learn the whole list at once.

_____ b. Copy definitions from the dictionary and memorize them.

_____ c. Ask your teacher to explain a word you don't understand.

_____ d. Think of clues to help you remember the word.

_____ e. Use flash cards to review.

_____ f. Practice the words many times for short periods of time.

CHAPTER 8: BEING A BETTER TEST-TAKER

On Friday, Tara was having a history test. The night before the test, she stayed up late studying. She couldn't decide what to study. Her mind jumped from one thing to another. Tara just knew she wouldn't do well.

On the day of the test, she overslept. She was almost late to school. She forgot to bring pencil and paper. As she started the test, she found questions she didn't know. She got more and more upset. When she got her test back, Tara had a low grade. She threw out the test without looking at it.

Jack studied for the test for a short time every day all week. He went over his notes. He made sure he knew all the vocabulary words. He learned the answers to the review questions.

The night before the test, Jack got a good night's sleep. He woke up in time to eat breakfast. During the test, he worked carefully. When he got his test back, he found his grade was better than the last time. He looked at his mistakes so he would know the answers next time.

WHAT HAPPENED?

Jack had learned how to do his best on tests. Tara needed to find out how to improve her test-taking skills.

WHAT DO YOU THINK?

Put an X on the line by each statement that tells about you.

_____ 1. I don't do well on tests.

_____ 2. I often stay up late studying for tests.

_____ 3. Sometimes I forget to bring pencil and paper to a test.

_____ 4. I never eat breakfast.

_____ 5. I can't think when I take a test.

_____ 6. I get really nervous when I have a test.

_____ 7. Sometimes I run out of time to finish a test.

_____ 8. I have trouble knowing what to study for tests.

How many statements did you mark?

If you marked even one, you can improve your test-taking skills.

PREPARING FOR A TEST

The most important part of test-taking happens before you enter the classroom on test day. Here are some ways to get ready for a test.

1. Start studying ahead of time. Begin reviewing the material as soon as you know the test date. Remember, many short study sessions work better than one long session.
2. Find out what will be on the test. Your teacher may also tell you what kind of test it will be (**true-false, essay, fill-in,** etc.).
3. Make sure you have your classroom notes, text notes, teacher handouts, and any other materials you need to study.
4. Go over your study materials. **Highlight,** or mark, all important points.
5. Review the material using the tips from Chapter 7. Repetition, mind pictures, grouping, rhyming, acronyms, and association will help you remember.
6. Go over and over the material until you know it.
7. Get a good night's sleep the night before the test.
8. The day of the test, eat a good breakfast.
9. Arrive at the test on time with everything you'll need to take the test (pencil, paper, calculator, etc.).

WHAT DO YOU THINK?

1. Why should you begin studying for a test as soon as you know the test date?

2. Why do you think eating breakfast or getting a good night's sleep could help you do better on a test?

3. Do you think students are likely to feel less anxious about taking a test if they are well prepared for the test? Explain your answer.

 Remember, being prepared is the most important part of good test-taking!

2 GENERAL TEST-TAKING HINTS

Once you've prepared well for a test, you can improve your test grades by using good test-taking skills.

1. Before you begin, scan the whole test. See what you have to do. Find out how many questions there are and how many points each one is worth.
2. Make a plan for taking the test. You should spend the most time on the test items that are worth the most points.
3. As you take the test, first answer questions that are easy. Mark questions you are not sure of. Don't waste a lot of time struggling with a hard question. Go back to it after you've finished the rest of the test.
4. If you finish early, review your answers.

WHAT DO YOU THINK?

1. Why do you think you should look over the whole test before you begin?

2. Why do you think it is a good idea to do the easy questions first?

3. Why is it usually a good idea to try to answer all questions on a test, even if you're not sure of the answers?

4. Why should you mark a question you're not sure of and go on with the test instead of spending more time on that question?

 Remember, look over the test before you begin, and plan your time.

3 TAKING TRUE-FALSE TESTS

True-false tests ask you to decide if a statement is true or false. Here are things to remember when you take a true-false test.

1. For a statement to be true, everything in the statement must be true.
2. If any part of a statement is false, the whole statement is false.
3. Read all true-false statements very carefully. Often one word in the statement will make the whole statement true or false.
4. Statements that include words like *always, never, no, every, all,* or *none* are often false.
5. Statements that include words like *usually, sometimes, most, often,* and *many* are often true.
6. If you are not sure about an answer, take a guess.
7. Be careful if the statement contains the word *not.* It will change the meaning of the sentence.

TRY IT OUT!
Write **True** or **False** on the line by each statement below.

_____ 1. A statement with the word *always* in it will always be true.

_____ 2. Answer *True* if a statement is mostly true.

_____ 3. The word *not* changes the meaning of a sentence.

_____ 4. A statement with the word *usually* is often true.

_____ 5. Leave all items you're not sure of blank.

_____ 6. One word can determine whether a statement is true or false.

_____ 7. You can read true-false questions faster than other kinds of questions.

_____ 8. Read statements containing the word *not* carefully.

_____ 9. For a statement to be true, everything in it must be true.

_____ 10. If part of a statement is false, the whole statement is false.

11. Some students think true-false tests are the easiest kind of test because you have the choice of only two answers. Do you agree? Explain your answer.

 Remember, read each statement on a true-false test very carefully.

4 TAKING MATCHING OR FILL-IN TESTS

Matching tests ask you to match words in one column with words or definitions in a second column. Here are things to do when taking a matching test.

1. Read the directions. See if an answer can be used more than once.
2. Before making any matches, read all items in both columns.
3. First make matches about which you are sure.
4. Cross out items you have used as you make matches.
5. Make your best guess for the items that are left.

TRY IT OUT!

Write the letter of the item in the second column on the line next to the word it matches.

_____ 1. Do this before you make any matches.

_____ 2. First make these matches.

_____ 3. Cross out these items.

_____ 4. Make your best guess on these.

a. items that are left

b. items you have used

c. matches you are sure of

d. Read all items in both columns.

On a fill-in test, each item has a part missing. You are to write the correct answer on the line. Here are things to do on a fill-in test:

1. Read the entire item. Think about what is missing.
2. Write an answer that completes the entire item.
3. The length of the line may be a clue to the length of the answer to be filled in.
4. After you have written your answer, reread the item to make sure your answer makes sense.

TRY IT OUT!

Fill in the blanks to complete each sentence.

5. On a fill-in test, read the _____ item before you write an answer.

6. The length of the line may be a clue to the _____ of the answer.

7. After you have written your answer, reread the entire item to make sure your answer makes _____ .

 Remember, on a matching test, read all items in both columns before making any matches. On a fill-in test, read over your answers to make sure they make sense.

5 TAKING MULTIPLE-CHOICE TESTS

Multiple-choice tests ask you to choose the correct answer from several options.
Here are things to do when taking a multiple-choice test.

1. As you read a multiple-choice question, try to think of the answer before you read the choices. If your answer is one of the choices, it is probably right.
2. Read all the choices before you choose. Don't just mark the first one that sounds good.
3. If you're not sure of an answer, try to narrow it down. Cross out choices you know are wrong. Then guess between the choices that are left.
4. Underline key words, such as *not, all, some,* or *except.* These words can change the answer.
5. If two of the choices are similar or opposites, one of them is probably the right answer.
6. Answer all questions. Don't leave anything blank.
7. Don't change an answer unless you are sure it is wrong.

TRY IT OUT!

Circle the letter of the correct answer below.

1. What should you do with key words in a multiple-choice question?

   a. Read them carefully.
   b. Underline them.
   c. Ignore them.
   d. Cross them out.

2. What should you do if you're not sure of an answer?

   a. Skip that question.
   b. Avoid guessing.
   c. Narrow down the choices.
   d. Ask the teacher.

3. If two answer choices are opposites,

   a. both are wrong.
   b. one is probably right.
   c. neither is right.
   d. mark another choice.

 Remember, on multiple-choice tests, read all the choices before you choose.

6 TAKING ESSAY TESTS

There is no one correct way to write the answer to an essay question. Here are some things to do when answering essay questions:

1. Read each essay question carefully. Decide how much time you'll need to answer each one. Answer the easiest questions first.
2. Be sure you understand what the question is asking. Pay special attention to direction words (see chart below).
3. Plan your answer before you write. Jot down ideas and facts that you are going to cover in your answer.
4. Write your answer neatly. Use complete sentences.
5. In your first sentence, give the main idea of what you will say.
6. Try not to leave an essay question blank. If you don't know the answer, take a few minutes to write something related to the subject. You may get partial credit for your answer.

Direction words tell you how to answer the essay question. Be sure you are giving the answer the essay question is asking for.

Direction Word	Meaning
compare	show how two or more things are alike
contrast	show how two or more things are different
evaluate	examine and give the worth of
explain	give causes or reasons
define	tell what something means
describe	give facts and details
summarize	give the main points about something

WHAT DO YOU THINK?

1. Why should you always try to write something for an essay question, even if you don't know much about the question?

(continued)

6 TAKING ESSAY TESTS *(continued)*

2. Why do you think it is important to know the meaning of direction words?

3. Why is it a good idea to answer the easiest questions first?

4. How would you answer these questions differently?

   a. Evaluate the new tax plan.

   b. Summarize the new tax plan.

5. Why do you think you should plan your answer before you write?

6. What information should be given in the first sentence of your answer?

 Remember, pay attention to direction words in answering essay questions.

TAKING STANDARDIZED TESTS

Most of the tests you take in school are made by your teachers. These tests cover material you have learned in class.

Standardized tests are long tests that have many questions. Answers are entered on computer answer sheets. People from all over a state or country take them. You may take a standardized test to graduate from high school. Colleges require standardized tests like the ACT or SAT. You take a standardized test to get a driver's license. These tests are required to get some kinds of jobs as well.

Here are some ways to do your best on standardized tests.

1. Find out as much as you can about what will be on the test.
2. Work on practice tests if they are available.
3. Get plenty of rest and eat a good breakfast the day of the test.
4. Be sure you understand the directions to the test. Read them carefully or listen as they are read to you. Ask questions if you don't understand.
5. Find out if you lose points for wrong answers. If so, don't guess. If not, answer all questions.
6. Look over the whole test first. See how many questions there are. Plan your time.
7. Start at the beginning of the test. The easiest questions often come first.
8. Mark the answer sheet neatly and carefully. Make no stray marks.

TRY IT OUT!

Mark the answers on the answer sheet below.

1. Ⓐ Ⓑ Ⓒ Ⓓ Ⓔ	3. Ⓐ Ⓑ Ⓒ Ⓓ Ⓔ	5. Ⓐ Ⓑ Ⓒ Ⓓ Ⓔ	7. Ⓐ Ⓑ Ⓒ Ⓓ Ⓔ
2. Ⓐ Ⓑ Ⓒ Ⓓ Ⓔ	4. Ⓐ Ⓑ Ⓒ Ⓓ Ⓔ	6. Ⓐ Ⓑ Ⓒ Ⓓ Ⓔ	8. Ⓐ Ⓑ Ⓒ Ⓓ Ⓔ

1. The easiest questions in a standardized test often come
   A. last
   B. in the middle
   C. first
   D. everywhere
   E. none of these

2. If you lose points for wrong answers
   A. guess
   B. don't guess
   C. guess only if you can narrow down your choices
   D. answer every question
   E. none of these

(continued)

7 TAKING STANDARDIZED TESTS *(continued)*

3. Before a test
   A. get a good night's sleep   D. read the directions
   B. eat a good breakfast   E. all of these
   C. do practice tests

4. Which of these is NOT a standardized test?
   A. college entrance exam   D. a chapter test in history
   B. teacher's license exam   E. none of these
   C. high-school graduation exam

5. How could you find out about what will be on the test?
   A. ask a teacher   C. study practice tests
   B. read a test prep book   D. all of the above

6. Why should you look over the whole test before you begin?
   A. to make you nervous   C. to help you plan your time
   B. to lose points   D. to make sure you know the answers

7. Where should you start a test?
   A. the middle   C. anywhere you want
   B. the end   D. the beginning

8. What should you do if you make stray marks on a test?
   A. leave them alone   C. cross them out
   B. erase them   D. make as many as you want

 Remember, practice tests can help you prepare for standardized tests.

8 TAKING TESTS AT SCHOOL

On Monday, a teacher gave the following instructions to the class:

> "We will have a test on Chapter Nine this Friday. Be sure you know all the vocabulary words on pages 212, 218, 223, and 227. Know the answers to the review questions on page 232. There will be two essay questions. Are there any questions on what will be on the test?"

WHAT DO YOU THINK?

1. Write one question you could ask the teacher about what will be on the test.

2. There are 25 vocabulary words that may be on the test. Tell how you would study the words.

3. There are 10 review questions on page 232. How would you learn the answers to those questions?

4. Tell what you are to do in each sample essay question:

   a. Contrast the qualifications for a senator and a representative.

   b. Describe the job of a party whip.

   c. Summarize how a bill is introduced in the Senate.

   d. Define the expressed and implied powers of Congress.

9 **TAKING A DRIVER'S LICENSE TEST**

 Donna planned to take the driver's **license** test when she turned 16. She got a copy of the *Driver's License Manual* from her state. It was 87 pages long! Donna was worried about passing the written test. It would be 20 multiple-choice questions covering the whole **manual.**

Put an X on the line by each thing Donna should do to prepare for the test.

_____ 1. Wait until the night before the test to begin studying, so the material will be fresh in her mind.

_____ 2. Get a good night's sleep before the test.

_____ 3. If she fails the test, she shouldn't worry about what she did wrong. She should just try again.

_____ 4. Review the manual for short periods over several weeks.

_____ 5. Know the answers to the review questions at the end of the manual.

_____ 6. She shouldn't use memory aids to help her remember driving facts.

_____ 7. When taking the test, she should mark answers she's not sure of and go back to them later.

_____ 8. If she fails the test, she should find out what questions she missed.

_____ 9. Answer the hard questions first. Then go back to the easy ones.

_____ 10. Not worry if she makes stray marks on the answer sheet.

_____ 11. Pick the first answer that sounds right to her and not read the others.

_____ 12. Underline key words, like *not.*

_____ 13. If she's not sure of an answer, try to narrow down the choices.

_____ 14. Always change her answer if she is later unsure of it.

10 TAKING A PLUMBER'S LICENSE TEST

Steve took a two-year course in plumbing in high school. When he graduated, he got a job as an **apprentice** plumber. Steve learned a lot on the job. After a while, he wanted to become a licensed plumber. To get a license, Steve would have to pass the state plumber's exam, a standardized test. Being a licensed plumber would allow Steve to do plumbing jobs on his own. It would also mean more pay. Steve really wanted to pass the exam!

WHAT DO YOU THINK?

1. Steve has already worked as a plumber. Do you think he needs to study for the exam anyway? Explain your answer.

2. Steve bought a book called *Preparing for the Plumber's Exam.* It was 300 pages long. How do you think Steve could organize his study time to cover all that material?

3. At the end of the book, there was a practice test. Steve had trouble on two of the five sections of the test. How could he use this information to help him pass the real exam?

4. Put an X by each thing Steve should do when taking the test.

_____ a. Look over the whole test first.
_____ b. Start at the beginning of the test.
_____ c. Do the hardest questions first.
_____ d. As he reads the choices, pick the first answer that seems right.
_____ e. Underline key words such as *never* or *always.*
_____ f. If he is not sure of an answer, try to narrow down the choices.
_____ g. Check over all his answers when he finishes the test.

11 USING YOUR LEARNING STYLE TO BE A BETTER TEST-TAKER

You can use your learning style to help you be a better test-taker. Here are a few suggestions:

Visual learner

Visual learners should make a list of topics and vocabulary likely to be on the test. They should read over their notes, highlighting important points.

Auditory learner

Auditory learners should make a tape of important facts and vocabulary to be learned. They should form a study group with friends. They might talk to the teacher about what will be on the test.

Kinesthetic learner

Kinesthetic learners should move around as they study. They should take frequent study breaks. They may wish to make charts of material to be learned.

Write your learning style here: _____

(visual, auditory, or kinesthetic)

Now answer each question below.

1. How might you use your learning style to plan a study session for a test?

2. How do you use your learning style to help you read the directions for a test?

3. How do you think you could use your learning style to help you prepare for a standardized test?

12 CHAPTER TEST

Fill in the answer sheet at the bottom of the page with the letter of the correct answer.

1. When taking a test,
   a. do the hardest questions first. They take the most time.
   b. if you finish early, hand in your test and relax.
   c. spend the most time on the items worth the most points.
   d. don't worry about how many questions there are on the test.

2. Which of these statements is true about true-false tests?
   a. Statements with *always* or *never* are usually true.
   b. Statements with *often* or *sometimes* are usually false.
   c. If any part of the statement is false, the whole statement is false.
   d. One word in a statement is not enough to make it false.

3. Which of these statements is true about matching or fill-in tests?
   a. Make matches about which you are sure first.
   b. The length of a line on a fill-in may be a clue.
   c. Make sure your answer on a fill-in uses correct grammar and makes sense.
   d. All of the above.

4. Which of these statements is true about essay questions?
   a. *Summarize* means to give the main points.
   b. *Contrast* means to tell how two or more things are alike.
   c. *Describe* means to give facts and details.
   d. A and C are true.

5. Which of these statements is true about multiple-choice tests?
   a. Mark the first choice that seems right.
   b. Never guess on this kind of test. Leave the answer blank.
   c. If two choices are opposites, one of them is probably the right answer.
   d. A and B are true.

6. Which of these is NOT a good way to prepare for a test?
   a. Eat a good breakfast.
   b. Highlight all important points in your notes.
   c. Use memory aids to help you remember the material.
   d. Stay up late studying to make sure you review everything.

1. Ⓐ Ⓑ Ⓒ Ⓓ	3. Ⓐ Ⓑ Ⓒ Ⓓ	5. Ⓐ Ⓑ Ⓒ Ⓓ
2. Ⓐ Ⓑ Ⓒ Ⓓ	4. Ⓐ Ⓑ Ⓒ Ⓓ	6. Ⓐ Ⓑ Ⓒ Ⓓ

 walch.com © 2003 Walch Publishing

Teacher's Guide

GETTING STARTED: USING YOUR LEARNING STYLE

BACKGROUND INFORMATION

Learning theory describes three main styles of learning: visual, auditory, and kinesthetic. Most of us learn through all three channels unless our senses are impaired. However, most of us have one primary sense that helps us learn the most. Some of your students will be primarily visual learners; others will be auditory or kinesthetic.

Students who are primarily visual learners learn best when they can see what they are learning. They may learn best by reading material over and over. Highlighting or underlining important information may be helpful to these students.

Students who are primarily auditory learners learn best when they can hear information. These students may find it helpful to review material out loud, possibly with a partner. Reading material out loud can be effective.

Students who are kinesthetic learners learn best by touching objects or by doing hands-on activities involving the material being taught. They may need to move around as they are studying.

Occasionally, some students will find that they have a mixed learning style. In that case, make sure the student understands that he or she will need to discover what is most useful from both styles.

Of course, all three modalities are useful to everyone in learning. The purpose of this discussion on learning styles is not to limit students' thinking to any one way of study. Rather, it is to make them aware that they may learn optimally in certain ways. Taking advantage of their natural learning styles will help students learn material easier and be more successful at school, at home, and on the job.

VOCABULARY

The teacher should go over the following words to make sure that each student can read them before beginning the chapter. Discuss the meaning of any words unfamiliar to the students. This procedure should be followed for each chapter in the book.

air filter	flash cards	learning style
aisle	highlight	outline
auditory	kinesthetic	stock
computer	laundry detergent	visual

ANSWERS

Getting Started: Using Your Learning Style (p. 1)

1. Tam was not using her learning style. Reading the words silently over and over just put her to sleep. It was not a good way for her to learn the words.

2. Tam found out that she learned best when she used her sense of hearing. She reviewed the words out loud. She listened to them repeated on a tape. This helped her remember the words.

A Learning Style Inventory (pp. 3–4)

Students can complete pages 3–4 on their own. When they are done, have them score their tests using the form on page 5.

Scoring Your Inventory (p. 5)

Students may score their own inventories. Most students will score some points in each category; however, most will be significantly higher in one. That category is their learning style. If a student has a score within two points on two learning styles, he or she has a mixed learning style. Explain to this student that he or she will need to use tips from both of these learning styles.

Tips for the Visual Learner (p. 6)

Answers will vary.

1. The visual learner can look at the flash cards and notes, then cover them and look again. The visual sense is being used over and over.

2. It may be easier for visual learners to organize their thoughts in writing.

3. The visual learner could put the words and their definitions on flash cards. Or the student could make a list of the words and their definitions. The definitions could be covered and checked until all words are learned.

Tips for the Auditory Learner (p. 7)

Answers will vary.

1. Two people studying together can review the material out loud. The auditory learner can hear the material over and over.

2. Auditory learners may express themselves better through oral rather than written means.

3. The auditory learner should write the words and their definitions on flash cards or in a list to review orally.

Tips for the Kinesthetic Learner (p. 8)

Answers will vary.

1. The kinesthetic learner needs to move around. Concentrating for short periods on the material to be learned, then taking a break and moving around is helpful.

2. Kinesthetic learners often express themselves best by creating something related to the material.

3. The kinesthetic learner may like to make flash cards and make up games while flipping through the cards. The student may wish to walk around the room while going through the cards.

Using Your Learning Style at School (p. 9)

1. a, b, c; 2. a, b; 3. a, b, c; 4. a, c, d; 5. a, b; 6. a, b, c

Using Your Learning Style at Home (p. 10)

1. Al might read the directions out loud. He may read them several times out loud until he understands the procedure. He may wish to have someone else read them to him as he works.

2. Joe might read the directions over several times to himself. He may wish to take the directions outside to look at as he works.

3. Amy might read each step of the directions and look at the mower to verify what each step means.

4. If it is done incorrectly, the mower may not work correctly, or it may be damaged.

Using Your Learning Style at Work *(p. 11)*

1. Maria could make a list or flash cards and go over them many times.

2. Jill might walk from aisle to aisle and read the signs indicating what is on each aisle.

3. Lin might do either of the above activities while saying the items aloud.

4. The stockers will be able to help customers better. They will be able to move quickly to the correct area to stock each item. Their boss will be pleased with their work.

Using Your Learning Style Test *(pp. 12–13)*

1. T 2. F; There are three main learning styles. 3. T 4. F; They prefer hands-on activities. 5. F; They prefer to read directions. 6. T 7. F; Moving around may be helpful. 8. T 9. T 10. F; They should read out loud whenever possible. 11. F; They should take frequent short breaks. 12. T 13. T 14. T 15. F; Highlighters can be used to mark ideas to be read over. 16. F; They usually prefer a written report. 17. F; Students with all three modalities can do equally well. 18. F; Kinesthetic learners may learn better to music. 19. F; It can be helpful at home and at work as well. 20. T 21. T 22. T 23. T 24. F; It is easy. Just take the inventory. 25. T

ADDITIONAL ACTIVITIES

1. Divide students into groups by learning style. Have them discuss ways to study for a test that they find most helpful. Each group should make a list to present to the class.

2. Have students read more about learning styles on the Internet. Students should write a paragraph about what they learned. These may be presented orally to the class.

3. Have students give the Learning Styles Inventory to another member of their family and make a list of how many students' family members have the same/different learning style as themselves.

4. Make a list of how many students in the class fall into the three categories of learning styles.

5. Have students write a paragraph detailing what they have learned about themselves from this chapter and how they might use this information to help them succeed in school.

CHAPTER 1: SETTING GOALS FOR YOURSELF

BACKGROUND INFORMATION

Explain to students the importance of having goals in life to help you focus and achieve things that are worthwhile. You may wish to use one of the following analogies:

1. A game of basketball would be pointless without a goal to shoot for.

2. One follows a path through the woods to reach the other side (the goal). Otherwise, you might get lost and wander in circles.

A goal should be something that is important to the individual. It should be specific, rather than vague; it should be described clearly and easy to measure. A goal should be realistic. Students should be aware that they may meet obstacles while working toward a goal, but they should not let that stop them. There are ways to overcome most obstacles.

It is not enough to set a goal; one must work hard to reach it. Long-term goals can be broken down into several short-term goals or steps. Students may need help identifying the steps for achieving a goal. Some helpful resources are books, magazines, teachers, and people knowledgeable in a given field.

Some students may wish to set a time line for reaching each step on the way to their goal. They may wish to mark these dates on their calendar.

VOCABULARY

estimate	landlord	realistic
focused	legal secretary	short-term goal
goal	long-term goal	specific
important	minimum wage	volunteer

ANSWERS

Setting Goals for Yourself *(p. 14)*

1. Because Jen had a goal, she was focused on working toward it. Thus, she spent a lot of her time working toward her goal.

2. If you have a goal you are working toward, some of your time and money will go toward achieving that goal. You will be working in a certain direction instead of drifting along.

3. Different people have different abilities and preferences. A good goal for one person might not be a good goal for someone else.

4. Answers will vary.

Making a Goal *(p. 15)*

1. If Kay makes $15 a week, that is only $60 a month. Even if that is enough to make the payments on the computer, she will have nothing left over for other expenses. She has no other savings. Kay needs to think about working more hours or looking for a less expensive computer.

2. Lou needs to think about his goal and make it more specific. He could set a goal of speaking in a friendly manner to his boss daily, for example.

Short- and Long-Term Goals *(p. 16)*

1. long 2. long 3. long 4. short 5. short 6. long 7. short 8. short

11–13. Answers will vary. Make sure answers are specific, realistic, and important to students.

Steps to Reaching Your Goal (p. 17)

1. Writing down your goal makes you think about it harder. If it is written down, you can more easily see if it is important, specific, and realistic.

2. If you see your goal daily, you will keep focused on it. You will not forget about it.

3. You should talk to your science teacher and make sure you know what a "C" project looks like. If you are having trouble getting organized, your teacher can lay out the steps for you.

4. You should talk to the track coach or a trained runner. This person should be able to help you set up a training regimen.

Breaking a Long-Term Goal into Steps (p. 18)

1. $410 2. $360 3. Mark should think about buying a less expensive car that he can afford.

Setting a Goal at School (p. 19)

1. Setting a goal is only a start. He also worked hard to achieve his goal. He had a plan.

2. Seeing the goal in writing reminded him of his goal on a daily basis. This helped him keep focused.

3. The track coach knew Tyrone was interested enough to ask how to improve. He got some good ideas how to improve. He could write these steps under his goal.

4. Steps might include: eating a balanced diet, getting plenty of rest, running increasing distances, buying good running shoes, working out with weights, finding a good place to run, and finding a friend to run with.

Setting a Goal at Home (p. 20)

1. c 2. b 3. a

4. Steps might include: reading an article on painting a room, talking to an expert painter at a paint shop, finding out what kind of paint is best for the job, measuring the room and determining how much paint is needed, getting a friend who is an experienced painter to help, gathering materials for painting, deciding what color he likes, preparing the room to be painted, and removing or covering furniture. (Numbering of the steps will depend on the students' answers.)

5. Yes. Once he learns the steps in painting, he should be able to learn as he paints.

Setting a Goal at Work (p. 21)

Students should put an X by 2, 4, 5, 7, 8, 10, 12, 13, 14, 16.

17. Val should write down her goal and keep working toward it.

Using Your Learning Style to Reach Your Goals (p. 22)

Answers will vary.

Chapter Test (p. 23)

1. Short-term goals can be reached in a short time, such as a day or a week. Long-term goals may take months or years.

2. Passing all your classes. Earning sufficient credits. Improving your learning strategies.

3. If a goal is not specific, you can't tell when you have reached it.

4. If a goal is not realistic, it will be frustrating if you can't reach it.

5. A goal helps you stay focused to work toward a specific end.

6. There could be many obstacles to reaching a goal; for example, wasting time or not having money.

7. You may need to examine your goal to see if it is realistic for you. If it is not, you may need to rethink your goal.

8. People who have goals achieve more because their efforts are directed.

9. Their goals may not be realistic. They may not realize they must work to reach their goals. The goal might not really be important to them.

10. Different people have different interests and abilities.

ADDITIONAL ACTIVITIES

1. Discuss with the class goals they have had in the past. Did they reach their goals? Did they give up?

2. Make a list of short-term goals students hope to reach this week. Under each goal, list the steps needed to reach the goal. Talk about resources needed to reach the goal.

3. Have students write a paragraph in which they explain their goals in each of the following areas: family, education, job, place to live, and leisure activities.

4. Divide students into groups. Each group is to think of four jobs that sound interesting. Then they should list steps a person might take who has a long-term goal of getting each of the jobs.

5. Assign students to interview someone who has an interesting job. Students should find out the steps needed to get that job. Have students report on their findings to the class.

6. Have students decide on a sport or skill they would like to learn. Have them make a list of steps they might follow to reach that goal.

7. Have students write a paragraph on one of the following topics:

   a. Setting a goal is like playing a game of basketball.
   b. Setting a goal is like choosing which path to take through the forest.
   c. Setting a goal is like following a compass or the North Star.

CHAPTER 2: GETTING ORGANIZED
BACKGROUND INFORMATION

Learning how to use your time wisely is a valuable life skill. Planning your time allows you more time to reach your goals. Learning to be more organized helps you avoid wasting time. These skills can help you be more successful in school, at home, and at work.

VOCABULARY

appointment	deadline	messages
avoid	interrupted	organized
calendar	interview	schedule

ANSWERS

Getting Organized (p. 24)

1. If she did the most important jobs first, she would have time to finish them. (By the time she finished the less important or optional jobs, she was out of time.)

2. You should work on the most important jobs or the jobs that are important for meeting your goals first. That way you can be sure they get done.

3. the biology test, picking up her brother, and soccer tryouts

4. the mall, the car wash, her nails and hair

Planning Your Time (p. 25)

1. 2   2. 1   3. 1   4. 3   5. 1   6. 3   7. 3

Making a Daily Schedule (p. 26)

1. 3–4 math tutoring; 4–5:30 basketball practice; 6–7 dinner/break; 7–9 study for history test

2. She is scheduling a definite time to be tutored in math and to study for the history test.

Using a Calendar (p. 27)

1. If you write things down on the appropriate date, you can see what needs to be done each day.

2. Answers will vary.

Organizing Your Space (p. 28)

1–2. Answers will vary.

3. You should be organized at work so you get everything done on time.

Avoiding Time Wasters (p. 29)

1. Each item listed should have an X by it.

2. Answers will vary.

Getting Organized at School (p. 30)

1. Answers will vary.

2. You don't waste time looking for lost items.

Getting Organized at Home (p. 31)

Students should put an X by 1, 2, 3, 5, 6, 11, 15.

Getting Organized at Work (p. 32)

1. Date: May 5

   Time: 8:15 A.M.

   To: Jeff Clem

   Message: Mike Marks called to set up a time for lunch.

   From: Mike Marks, 555-4455 (H) or 555-3423 (W)

   Person taking message: Student's name

2. Date: January 23

   Time: 4:15 P.M.

To: Carlos

Message: Your mother called to say your brother is in River Hospital. She has gone to the hospital.

From: Your mom, 555-3509 (hospital)

Person taking message: Student's name

Using Your Learning Style to Get Organized (p. 33)

Answers will vary.

Chapter Test (p. 34)

Explanations of answers will vary.

1. No. Put the jobs on the list in order of importance (1, 2, 3), then do the most important ones first.

2. No. A schedule should be in larger blocks of time, such as an hour or half hour.

3. Yes. You should estimate how much time each job will take to fit it into your schedule.

4. Yes. That way you can do the most important jobs first.

5. Yes. That way it is easier to remember important information.

6. No. Assignments should be written in an assignment notebook. Slips of paper are easy to lose.

7. Yes. That way you are ready to go in the morning.

8. Yes. It'll be easier to find the papers you need.

ADDITIONAL ACTIVITIES

1. Ask students to name ways they find themselves wasting time. Make a list of these on the board.

2. Discuss daydreaming. Have students divide into groups and come up with ways students could avoid daydreaming. Make a list of each group's answers on the board.

3. Have students write a paragraph on the following topic: My goals affect how I use my time.

4. Have students create a calendar and a To Do list form on the computer.

5. Have students write a paragraph about a time when they didn't plan their time well and what happened as a result. Students may volunteer to read these aloud to the class.

CHAPTER 3: KNOWING WHERE TO GET INFORMATION

BACKGROUND INFORMATION

Knowing where to get information is a vital skill for independent living. It is also a very broad skill and one that is learned over time. This chapter seeks to start young people thinking about some of the ways they can get information to help them solve problems they may encounter at school, home, and work. Students will also learn that there is more than one way to get information. They may need to try several things before they get the information they need.

VOCABULARY

agencies	debt	quotation marks
almanac	dictionary	reference book
alphabetical	employment agency	resources
atlas	encyclopedia	résumé
broad	fiction	search engine
call number	Internet	shelter
catalog	learning disability	thesaurus
classified ads	librarian	tutoring
community college	narrow	utilities
community services	nonfiction	web site
credit counselor	opinion	

ANSWERS

Knowing Where to Get Information *(p. 35)*

1. local government agencies, library, schools, etc.

2. utilities, bus schedule, bank

3. community college, reading about learning disability, soccer, bird-watching

Getting Information from the Telephone Book *(p. 36)*

1. 555-9870; 2. 555-4998; 3. 555-4498; 4. 555-0087;
5. 555-4356; 6. 555-3388; 7. 555-4903; 8. 555-8375 9. 911

Getting Information from the Newspaper *(p. 37)*

1. a. 4B; b. 1D; c. 4–5E; d. 4E; e. 1G; f. 1B

2. You can buy and sell things, find a job, find an apartment, etc.

Getting Information at the Library *(p. 38)*

1. The librarian could have explained where to look for information.

2. If she goes in at a time that is not busy, the librarian can spend more time with her and show her how to find things.

3. Yes. The library is there for everyone to use. It provides a much wider range of information than any one person could have.

Getting Information from Reference Books *(p. 39)*

1. newspaper 2. atlas 3. dictionary 4. encyclopedia
5. dictionary 6. atlas 7. magazine 8. newspaper
9. thesaurus 10. almanac

Getting Books in the Library *(p. 40)*

1. It tells where the book is located.

2. You would need to try a different name for the subject. If you still can't find it, ask for help.

3. You can find the book if you know its title, author, or subject.

4. Ask the librarian for help.

Getting Information from the Internet *(p. 41)*

1. Answers will vary. Samples are: a. Robert Redford
b. the Miami Dolphins
2. "football + rules"
3. Marcus used information from a site that was not reliable.

Getting Information from People *(p. 42)*

1. You can compare and choose the best offer.

2. Other people may know of a vacancy that is not listed anywhere.

3. Your teacher may offer tutoring. If not, your counselor will probably know where tutoring is offered in the community.

Getting Information at School *(p. 43)*

1. read books or encyclopedias, watch videos, interview a veteran; Explanations will vary.

2. at the public library or school library

3. your school counselor, librarian, a friend, the community college

4. school, library, a friend's house

5. read books or magazine articles, visit banks, use the Internet; Explanations will vary.

6. read books, watch videos, talk to someone who plays well, take lessons, use the Internet

7. visit museums, read books, use the Internet, talk to artists, take classes, etc.

Getting Information at Home *(p. 44)*

1. get references from friends and neighbors

2. read magazine articles, talk to repairperson, read *Consumer Reports*

3. IRS tax service, free help at library

4. the Internet, cookbooks at library, friends

5. consumer credit counselor, bank

6. friends, newspapers, phone book

7. newspapers, radio, the Internet

Getting Information at Work *(p. 45)*

1. ask the boss or a coworker, read the employee handbook

2. call the community college or the library

3. ask a coworker, ask the boss, read the employee handbook

4. ask a coworker

5. ask friends, read the classified ads in the newspaper, use the Internet

6. get a book that shows how, look on the Internet for samples, ask a teacher

7. ask the worker who gave you the application

Using Your Learning Style to Get Information *(p. 46)*

Answers will vary.

Chapter Test *(p. 47)*

1. F It is better to find out the correct way to do the job.
2. T 3. T 4. F Librarians are also there to help people find what they need. 5. F Look in an atlas. 6. T 7. F They are listed by call number. 8. T 9. F Anyone can put information on the Internet. 10. F The bank will give information for free. 11. F Friends can be a good source of job leads.
12. F It lists a variety of basic services, such as schools, utilities, and government services. 13. T 14. F Use the dictionary. 15. T 16. F All books in the library have a call number. 17. T 18. T 19. T 20. T 21. F Use newspapers

or magazines. 22. F It also gives pronunciation and part of speech.

ADDITIONAL ACTIVITIES

1. Have students work in groups to make lists of information found in the phone book.
2. Have a librarian speak to the class about information resources available in the library.
3. Discuss the blue pages of the phone book that list government agencies.
4. Take students to the library. Show them how books are organized on the shelves.
5. Have students look for information on the Internet.
6. Have students practice narrowing their search.
7. Have students report on types of information/stories found in various parts of the newspaper.
8. Have students try finding the same type of information on several search engines, such as Google or Yahoo!

CHAPTER 4: GETTING INFORMATION FROM BOOKS

BACKGROUND INFORMATION

Textbooks are organized to provide a great deal of information in addition to the actual text. The table of contents gives a good overview of the main topics in the book. The index gives a detailed alphabetical listing of topics in the book and the pages where they are found. The title page lists title, author, and publisher, while the copyright page gives the date of publication. Some books have an appendix that gives information not included in the body of the text. Other books have a bibliography that lists sources used by the author in preparing the text. The glossary defines terms as they are used in the text.

Many visual aids are found in books. Chapter 4 includes bar graphs, pie charts, and charts. Other kinds of visual aids are pictures, photographs, drawings, pictographs, line graphs, diagrams, flowcharts, time lines, and maps.

Some books contain other features not covered in *Learning Strategies for School, Home, and Work*. A frontispiece is a full-page illustration facing the title page. The preface (also called the foreword or introduction) is material at the beginning of a book in which the author, editor, or publisher explains the purpose and scope of the book. The preface may also contain acknowledgments. Some books contain a list of illustrations (maps, diagrams, charts, etc).

VOCABULARY

agriculture	education	religion
antislavery	element	sonar
appendix	emergencies	table of contents
astronomer	glossary	terminate
author	index	title page
bar graph	literature	visual aids
bibliography	pie chart	
copyright page	publisher	

ANSWERS

Getting Information from Books (p. 49)

1. Keisha needs to learn how to use the index. The table of contents might have pointed her to the right chapter.
2. Answers will vary.
3. You can locate things you need quickly. You can take advantage of the features the author has put in the book to make it easier to use.
4. A road map is a guide that takes you places you want to go. An index takes you to the place you want to go in a book.

Knowing the Parts of a Book (p. 50)

1. glossary 2. index 3. copyright page 4. title page
5. table of contents 6. appendix

Using the Table of Contents (p. 51)

1. Chapter 1 2. Chapter 2 3. Chapter 4 4. Chapter 3
5. Chapter 4 6. Chapter 3 7. Chapter 1 8. Chapter 1
9. Chapter 2 10. Chapter 2 11. Chapter 3

Using the Index (p. 52)

1. 125 2. 167 3. 58–59 4. 64–65 5. 599 6. 686–687
7. 198–199 8. 172 9. 359

Reading a Bar Graph (p. 53)

1. The bars show how many miles an hour each animal can run.
2. (any two) antelope, roe deer, cheetah
3. Graphs give important information that may not be included in the text.

Reading a Pie Chart (p. 54)

1. It gives the percent of different elements in the human body.
2. Each slice stands for a different element or group of elements.
3. oxygen
4. "Other" is a total of parts too small to be pictured individually on the chart. It represents other elements that are found in the human body but are not listed separately on the chart.
5. Answers will vary.

Getting Information from Books at School (p. 55)

1. the meaning as it is used in the text
2. The dictionary entry gives pronunciation, part of speech, and multiple meanings of the word; the glossary lists only the meaning as used in the text.
3. The glossary is the better choice. It will be easier to get the correct meanings of the words as used in the text.
4. You would have to read all the definitions given in the dictionary and decide which one was the correct definition.

Getting Information from Books at Home *(p. 56–57)*

1. It compares the features and costs of three cell-phone plans.
2. Telright and Easyphone
3. Telright and Easyphone
4. Phonecheap
5. Easyphone
6. Phonecheap
7. Easyphone
8. Easyphone
9. Phonecheap
10. Answers will vary.
11. Answers will vary.
12. Answers will vary.

Getting Information from Books at Work *(p. 58)*

1. It gives the company rules.
2. The employee will know what the company expects of employees.
3. The employee can look up what to do in different situations.
4. a. 16 b. 32 c. 16 d. 24 e. 17 f. 14 g. 34 h. 23 i. 19 j. 14

Using Your Learning Style to Get Information from Books *(p. 59)*

Answers will vary.

Chapter Test *(p. 60–61)*

1. T 2. F; The author is listed on the title page.
3. F; It lists title, author, and publisher. 4. F; It lists sources used by the author. 5. T 6. F; It lists only key words in the text. 7. F; Look on the copyright page. 8. T 9. F; Most textbooks have both. 10. T 11. F; Visual aids can be graphs, charts, drawings, photos, etc. 12. T 13. T 14. T 15. T 16. T 17. F; Use the glossary. 18. T 19. T 20. F; It lists topics in the book in alphabetical order.

ADDITIONAL ACTIVITIES

1. Make up a list of topics that can be found in the table of contents in a textbook your students use. Have students work in groups to find all the topics. Discuss the groups' findings.
2. On the board, write a list of 20 topics found in the index of a textbook used by your students. Have students locate the page on which each topic can be found. This could be a group activity.
3. Have students write the definitions of five words from the glossary of one of their textbooks. Then have them look up the same words in a dictionary. Ask for volunteers to read their pairs of definitions aloud. Compare the definitions.
4. Have students work in groups to make a list of all the visual aids they find in their textbook. Compile their answers to make one list on the board.
5. Allow students to have a race to see who can locate information in the book the fastest. Students could be divided into teams, with a team scoring a point when one of its members is first to find the requested item.
6. Have students make a chart comparing three of their textbooks. They should look to see if each book has a title page, copyright page, table of contents, bibliography, index, appendix, glossary, preface, and list of maps. Below is a sample chart.

	Modern Biology	*Algebra One*	*Geography for Today*
Table of contents			
Title page			
Copyright page			
Bibliography			
Index			
Appendix			
Glossary			
List of maps			
Preface			

CHAPTER 5: UNDERSTANDING WHAT YOU READ

BACKGROUND INFORMATION

Chapter 5 presents a system for reading textbooks (and other material) called Active Reading. Active Reading will help students understand and remember more of what they read. Using this system ensures that the student is actually going over the material three times instead of once. First, they scan the material, reading the title, headings, words in italics or bold print, visual aids, and summary. Next, they read the material, turning each heading into a question and making sure they can answer the question after they finish reading. They also make sure they know the meaning of each word in italics or bold print. Finally, students review the material by scanning it and stating the main idea of the material under each heading.

VOCABULARY

active	evaluated	purchase
Allies	focus	review
amendment	italic	scan
Aqua-Lung	initial employment period	scuba
bold	installation	sick days
citizen	option	suffrage
defect	personal days	terminated
employee	pollution	valid
employer		warranty

ANSWERS

Understanding What You Read (p. 62)

1. He read the newspaper, television schedule, directions, and the employee handbook.
2. His mind wandered. He lost his place. He forgot what he read.
3–5. Answers will vary.

Being an Active Reader (p. 63)

1. Scanning gives you the main idea of the material. It gives you an overview.
2. It gives you a purpose because you are reading to answer the question.
3. You are going over the material another time to be sure you understand it.

Active Reading Step 1: Scan (p. 64)

1. Jacques Cousteau
2. Allies, Aqua-Lung, scuba, pollution
3. The life of Jacques Cousteau

Active Reading Step 2: Read (p. 65)

1. a. Why did he learn to love the sea? b. What did he invent? When was he a spy? c. What kind of movies did he make? d. What is the *Calypso?*
2. a. Allies: In World War II, these nations allied against the Axis. b. Aqua-Lung: a trademark for scuba equipment; c. scuba: a device containing compressed air used for breathing underwater (self-contained underwater breathing apparatus) d. pollution: contaminated air, water, or soil

Active Reading Step 3: Review (p. 66)

1. Once they have read the material, they feel that they are done. They may not see the use of spending extra time reviewing.
2. You will understand and remember the material better.
3. To state it in your own words, you must understand the section.
4. Only important words are in bold print. Therefore, to understand the meaning of a section, you must know the meanings of the words in bold print.

Understanding What You Read at School (p. 67)

1. amendments passed as a result of the Civil War
2. thirteenth   3. fifteenth   4. fourteenth
5. Students should put an X by a white man.

Understanding What You Read at Home (p. 68)

1. a. Yes. The warranty lasts one year regardless of the price paid.
   b. No. The warranty does not cover damage caused by incorrect installation.
   c. No. The warranty is not good on products purchased in Canada.
   d. No. That would be 13 months after purchase.
   e. No. The warranty does not cover damage caused by water.
2. nothing

Understanding What You Read at Work (p. 69)

1. If the employee is not working out, he or she can be fired. It is also a time to help employees learn to do their jobs well.
2. The employee will not be paid for this time.
3. The employee will be given a chance to improve. If this does not happen, the employee may be fired.
4. The employee will be evaluated. The employee can now use sick or personal days.
5. nothing
6. To know how to keep your job and avoid loss of pay.

Using Your Learning Style to Understand What You Read (p. 70)

Answers will vary.

Chapter Test (p. 71)

1. a. scan b. read c. review
2. You scan to get a quick overview or main idea of what the material will be about.
3. To give yourself a purpose for reading the section.
4. By going over it once more, you increase your chances of remembering it.
5. Make sure you understand the meaning of that word by the time you've finished reading.

6. Active Reading allows you to focus better. You are going over the material three times.

7. a. the title b. the headings c. words in bold or italic print d. the summary

ADDITIONAL ACTIVITIES

1. Have students look through one of their textbooks and choose a section to practice on using Active Reading. Have them identify the title, headings, words in bold or italics, and summary (if any). Have them try out reading the section using the Active Reading technique. Discuss how it felt to use the technique when reading their book.

2. Choose a textbook. Write headings from it on the board. Have students practice turning these into questions.

3. Divide students into groups. Have each group choose 10 headings from a textbook and turn each into a question. Have a student from each group present the group's list to the class.

4. Have students list examples of Active Reading at home or at work. (examples: reading a medicine label, reading a care label on an article of clothing, reading a manual for operating equipment, etc.)

CHAPTER 6: LEARNING TO TAKE NOTES
BACKGROUND INFORMATION

Tests often cover material that has been presented in class. So it is important to have good notes from which to study. Many students are not active listeners, a skill vital to taking notes. To be an active listener, the student must do more than just hear the teacher. He or she must listen, think about what is being said, and try to understand it. Students must also avoid distractions, such as daydreaming, looking out the window, and paying attention to other students.

Taking notes helps you focus on what is being said. It is not possible or desirable to write down everything that is said. Students must learn to pick out important points. These are often preceded by clues, such as "the important point is" or "there are three reasons." Students should write down material presented on the board or overhead.

The notes should be easy to read. To take notes faster, students may use abbreviations or symbols. A pencil or erasable pen will help keep notes neat.

Students should get in the habit of going over their notes as soon as possible after class. This way, the material is still fresh in their minds. Students may need to rewrite their notes if they are not clear.

Students should realize that it is their responsibility to get notes if they miss class.

VOCABULARY

abbreviations	landscaping	shrub
active	legend	symbol
archaeologist	mulch	tamp
distracted	passive	

ANSWERS

Learning to Take Notes (p. 72)

1. Pat was not thinking about what she heard. She tried to write it all down and missed the main points.

2. José did not take any notes.

3. Jamal was not paying attention and missed much of what was said.

4. Material from class may be on the test. Notes give you something to study from.

5. Answers will vary.

Being an Active Listener (p. 73)

1. Passive listening means the ears receive the sounds; active listening means you pay attention and interpret them.

2. Answers will vary.

3. Answers will vary.

4. The active listener is thinking about what is being said and will therefore pick up the important points.

Taking Good Notes (p. 74)

1. You should ask for the information to be explained.

2. If the teacher takes the time to write things on the board, that is a signal that they are important.

3. Answers will vary.

4. Reviewing helps you remember the material. It also gives you a chance to make corrections or additions while the material is fresh in your mind. Rewriting allows you to make any needed corrections or additions.

Following the Clues to Take Good Notes (p. 75)

1. Numbers are a guideline. If the teacher says there are three main points, be sure you have all three.

2. Answers will vary.

3. Whenever a clue is used, you would be sure to write down what follows.

4. You will know to write down what follows a clue.

5. Answers will vary.

Using Abbreviations and Symbols in Your Notes (p. 76)

1. Answers will vary. Accept reasonable variations.

2. a. temp $\uparrow$ b. cereal w/ raisins c. war w/o honor d. price $\neq$ quality

Reviewing and Rewriting Your Notes (p. 77)

The giant panda is endangered. There are less than 1,000 in the wild. Adults are more than six feet tall and weigh over 220 pounds. At birth, the giant panda is smaller than a rat. The giant panda's most important food is bamboo.

Taking Notes at School (p. 78)

Accept all reasonable alternatives to the notes below:

* true legend = story of Troy
Homer, ancient poet, wrote of Greek-Trojan war
War > 10 years
Greeks made large horse — peace offering

Trojans pulled it in. Inside 100s warriors. Trojans killed. War ended.

1873 archaeologist Schliemann found ruins proven to be Troy

Taking Notes at Home (p. 79)

Accept any reasonable variations:

1. Saw brkn limbs ↓ break. Roof tar on cut. Or Prune Stop. > 2 coats.

2. Min. dep. $25. No interest. $3 if bal. ↓ $25. 20¢ each check. Free ATM card.

3. You will remember all the details if you have them written down.

Taking Notes at Work (p. 80)

Accept reasonable alternatives:

1. Plant late winter, early spring. Hole 2X width and 2X depth of rootball. Put shrub in. Tamp soil. Water. Mulch 2–3" (peat moss, pine bark). Don't overwater. Let soil dry out between waterings.

2. You want to remember all instructions correctly and not forget anything.

3. You might have a small notebook for all work notes.

Using Your Learning Style to Take Notes (p. 81)

Answers will vary.

Chapter Test (p. 82)

1. An active listener is thinking about and trying to understand what is said. A passive listener just hears.

2. Answers will vary.

3. You can make corrections or additions. It cements the ideas in your mind.

4. a. ↓ b. b/c c. esp d. * e. w/o

5. If the teacher takes the time to write it down, it is important.

6. You can make changes neatly.

7. Numbers are a reference point to make sure you have all the ideas presented.

8. (any two) daydreaming, looking out window, talking, etc.

ADDITIONAL ACTIVITIES

1. Give "mini lectures" of one minute or less and have students take notes. Let them compare and critique each other's notes.

2. Assign students to make a list of clues their teachers use in a one-day period that signal something important to come. The next day, make a list of these clues on the board.

3. Have students make posters illustrating note-taking skills.

4. Have students practice taking notes on telephone messages. Students may role-play this activity with one person being the caller and the other taking the notes.

5. Have students write a three-paragraph essay in which they describe: how they get ready to take notes in class, how they take the notes in class, and what they do with the notes after class.

6. Have students write a paragraph about how to take notes. Ask them to use signal words in the paragraph and to underline these.

7. Write a list of polysyllabic words on the board (e.g., December, amendment, library). Have students make up abbreviations for each of these words that they could use in note-taking.

8. Have students take turns coming to the board to write sentences using abbreviations and symbols. Allow another student to decode the sentence.

CHAPTER 7: REMEMBERING WHAT YOU LEARN

BACKGROUND INFORMATION

Many students do not achieve what they are capable of in school because they lack an organized approach for remembering what they learn. This chapter will teach basic skills everyone can use to improve memory. Students will learn simple ways to remember words, memorize longer passages, remember what they read, and ways to apply these skills at school, home, and work.

A good deal of research in the field of learning gives us basic concepts about memory. You learn things better when you are motivated to do so. You learn better by being actively involved in the learning process (taking notes, reading aloud, or discussing). Reviewing improves retention. Remembering is easier when the material makes sense. A number of short study sessions is more effective than one long study session.

When learning new vocabulary words, students should first make sure they understand what the word means. Flash cards are a good way to review. Auditory learners may wish to review with a friend. Visual learners may wish to write the word and its meaning. Students may wish to look for clues to help them remember the word. For example, if a student knows that the prefix "bi-" means "two," it is easier to remember that *binomial* is an expression with two terms.

When memorizing a longer passage, students should first read the entire passage and make sure they understand it. They should look up all new vocabulary. Then the passage should be broken into sections and learned in order, one section at a time. Once the material is learned, it is important to keep reviewing it.

Remembering what is read can be easier using the Active Reading system that was presented in Chapter 5. Students should scan over the entire selection quickly. Then they should read a short section, turning the heading into a question. They should then write down the answer to their question in their notes, as well as any words in bold or italic print and their meanings. All notes should be in the student's own words. After the entire selection is read, students should review their notes to see whether they included all important points. Following this process will make remembering easier.

Six memory aids are discussed in this chapter: repetition, mind pictures, grouping, rhyming, acronyms, and association.

VOCABULARY

acronym	memorize	rhyming
association	mind pictures	security deposit
furnished	passage	utilities
grouping	repetition	vocabulary
lease		

ANSWERS

Remembering What You Learn (p. 83)

1. If you really want to learn something, you will be focused on it. You will not mind going over and over it. You will keep at it until you've mastered it.

2. If you understand what something means, you can tie it to other things you know. If you are just memorizing words that don't make sense, they will be very hard to remember.

3. If you work too long at one time, your brain becomes tired, you are not focusing as well, and you end up wasting time. Short, focused repetition works best.

Remembering Vocabulary Words (p. 84)

1. False. Clues are a great way to remember.
2. True.
3. True.
4. False. Write the definition in your own words.

Remembering What You Read (p. 85)

1. The answer to that question will be the main idea of that section.

2. The words are in bold or italic print because they are important for you to remember.

3. It is best to think about the meaning and put it in your own words.

4. You are actively involved with the material by reading, thinking, and writing.

Remembering Longer Passages (p. 86)

Students should put an X by 1, 2, 4, 5, 7.

Remembering Using Repetition and Mind Pictures (p. 87)

1. Answers will vary.
2. Answers will vary.

Remembering Using Grouping and Rhyming (p. 88)

1. Answers will vary.

2. The second list is easier because the words are organized into groups, and each group is in alphabetical order.

3. Answers will vary. Sample answers:

    a. The world's first flight was by the brothers Wright!

    b. An assembly-line factory made the Model T!

Remembering Using Acronyms and Association (p. 89)

1. a. MOP; b. LAMP

2. a. Associate the name *Diesel* with diesel mechanic, diesel fuel, or diesel engine.

    b. Associate the name *Kuhl* (*cool*) with snow.

Remembering at School (pp. 90–91)

1. a. Smog is made from smoke and fog. b. The French and Indian War began in 1754.

2. a. FAR b. LAST

3. a. Animals are found in a zoo(logy). b. Tools are made of iron.

4. mammals: key deer, grizzly bear, woodland caribou, Louisiana black bear

    birds: California condor, whooping crane, bald eagle, ivory-billed woodpecker

    reptiles/amphibians: American alligator, American crocodile, Wyoming toad, Kemp's ridley sea turtle

    fish: snail darter, bull trout, Chinook salmon, desert pupfish

5. Answers will vary.

Remembering at Home (p. 92)

1. a. furnished: Furniture is provided.

    b. unfurnished: The apartment does not have furniture in it.

    c. utilities: electricity, gas, water, etc.

    d. security deposit: This is an amount you pay before you move in to cover possible future damage. If no damage is done to the apartment, it is refunded when you move out.

    e. lease: an agreement that you will rent the apartment for a certain amount of time

2. See chart below.

3. Apartment #3 looks the best since all utilities are included, it is furnished, and has two bedrooms.

	Apartment #1	Apartment #2	Apartment #3
Furnished or unfurnished	furnished	unfurnished	furnished
Number of bedrooms	1	1	2
Amount of rent	$325	$425	$425
Amount of security deposit	$325	$300	$350
Utilities included?	water only	water only	all utilities included
Length of lease	1 year	6 months	1 year

Remembering at Work (*p. 93*)

1. Students should put an X by a, c, d, e, g, h.

2. Students should put an X by a, b, c, e.

3. To keep his job.

Using Your Learning Style to Remember What You Learn (*p. 94*)

Answers will vary.

Chapter Test (*p. 95*)

1. a. acronym b. association c. grouping d. mind picture e. rhyming f. repetition

2. Students should put an X by c, d, e.

3. You are going over the material several ways at once: hearing, writing, and seeing it. You are actively involved in the learning process.

4. Students should put an X by c, d, e, f.

ADDITIONAL ACTIVITIES

1. Play memory games to demonstrate the power of organization. Say a series of numbers out loud, such as 9, 4, 3, 6, 4, 5, 7, 5, 4, 1, 0. Ask students to write down as many numbers as they can remember. Repeat the activity, placing the numbers in a logical order such as 2, 4, 6, 8, 10.
   Have students write these down. Point out how much easier it is to learn when things are organized. Repeat this game by placing a variety of objects on a tray.

2. Another memory game students may enjoy is: "I went on vacation, and in my suitcase I took . . ." The teacher says this sentence and adds a finisher. The next person repeats what the teacher says and adds one more thing. The game continues around the room.

3. Have students keep a list of memory techniques they have used during a one-week period to do homework or study for tests.

4. Make up a list of 10 vocabulary words you think will be unfamiliar to students. Lead them through the recommended learning process for new vocabulary words.

5. Have students construct flash cards to study the words in #4.

6. Have each student choose a poem to learn using the techniques from page 86.

7. Have students read a short selection, then answer questions without referring back to it. Repeat this activity, allowing students to take notes on the selection before answering questions. Compare their success rate.

8. Give students additional opportunities to practice the process of reading and taking notes.

9. Give students practice finding the main idea of a paragraph.

10. Have students write an ad for an imaginary product in which they use repetition, rhyme, etc. to catch the potential customer's attention.

11. Have students make up rhymes, acronyms, etc. for material they are currently studying in one of their classes. Allow students to share these with the class.

12. Give students a series of instructions that they are to remember. They may take notes on the instructions. Then have them complete the instructions.

13. Give students directions for drawing a scene that includes many details. They may take notes as you talk. Allow them to draw the scene. See how many of the details they remember.

14. Have students practice taking messages that are given to them over the phone, as might occur in many job situations. They may exchange messages and check each other's work.

15. Give students a list of items to buy at the store. They may take notes. Check for accuracy.

CHAPTER 8: BEING A BETTER TEST-TAKER

BACKGROUND INFORMATION

In order to do well on tests, students must study hard and be prepared (see Chapter 7). Once they have done that, they can improve their performance on tests by learning test-taking strategies.

It is important for students to realize that they will need to take tests throughout life, not just in school. Tests may be given to get a job, get advancement on the job, get a driver's license, etc.

VOCABULARY

apprentice	evaluate	matching
compare	explain	multiple choice
contrast	fill-in	penalty
define	highlight	standardized test
describe	license	summarize
essay	manual	true-false

ANSWERS

Being a Better Test-Taker (*p. 96*)

Answers will vary.

Preparing for a Test (*p. 97*)

1. It is more effective to study in short sessions over a period of time.

2. You will have more energy. You will not be distracted by feeling hungry or tired.

3. Yes. You will be less nervous if you know that you really know the material.

General Test-Taking Hints (*p. 98*)

1. You can plan your time better. You won't be surprised by an essay question worth a lot of points at the end of the test.

2. It may give you a feeling of confidence. You will be sure to have time to complete all the ones you know.

3. You may get some of them right, or get partial credit.

4. It isn't a good idea to waste too much time puzzling over a question you're not sure of and possibly not have time to finish other parts of the test.

Taking True-False Tests (p. 99)

1. False 2. False 3. True 4. True 5. False 6. True 7. False
8. True 9. True 10. True 11. Answers will vary.

Taking Matching or Fill-in Tests (p. 100)

1. d 2. c 3. b 4. a 5. entire 6. length 7. sense

Taking Multiple-Choice Tests (p. 101)

1. b 2. c 3. b

Taking Essay Tests (pp. 102–103)

1. You may write something connected to the question and thus get partial credit.

2. If you don't follow the directions, you may lose all or partial credit.

3. This way you can be sure to have plenty of time to give a good, complete answer.

4. a. If you evaluate the new tax plan, you examine it and talk about its worth. So you are giving your opinion whether the plan is a good one.
   b. If you summarize the tax plan, you are listing the main points of the plan. You are not necessarily giving your opinion of it.

5. to write an organized answer and include all important points

6. the main idea of what you plan to say

Taking Standardized Tests (pp. 104–105)

1. C 2. B 3. E 4. D 5. D 6. C 7. D 8. B

Taking Tests at School (p. 106)

1. Answers will vary.

2. Make a list of the words. Look up their definitions and write them in your own words.
   Put the words on flash cards and review them over and over.

3. Write the answers to the review questions. Go over them until you know them.

4. a. Tell how the qualifications are different.
   b. Give facts and details about the party whip's job.
   c. Give the main points about how a bill is introduced in the Senate.
   d. Tell what expressed and implied powers are.

Taking a Driver's License Test (p. 107)

Students should put an X by the following statements: 2, 4, 5, 7, 8, 12, 13.

Taking a Plumber's License Test (p. 139)

1. Yes. Steve probably knows a lot about plumbing already. But there is probably information on the test that he does not know.

2. Steve should set aside several blocks of time during the week. He could work on one chapter at a time, moving on to the next chapter when he has mastered the previous chapter.

3. Steve should spend extra time studying the sections that gave him trouble.

4. Students should put an X by a, b, e, f, g.

Using Your Learning Style to Be a Better Test-Taker (p. 109)

Answers will vary.

Chapter Test (p. 110)

1. c 2. c 3. d 4. d 5. c 6. d

ADDITIONAL ACTIVITIES

1. Ask students how they feel about taking tests.

2. Have students write a paragraph about how they feel about test-taking.

3. Discuss test anxiety. A little anxiety can help you focus and do your best. Excessive anxiety will lower your test score. To reduce test anxiety, students should start studying early. Cramming will increase test anxiety. Discuss relaxation techniques students could try.

4. Have students make posters illustrating a test-taking skill.

5. Students may wish to bring in old tests from other classes that illustrate some of the hints included in this chapter for doing certain types of tests.

6. Have students work in groups to make a list of things they have learned about test-taking from this chapter. Each group should present their list to the class.

7. Discuss times when you would have to take a test at home or at work. Make a list on the board.

Appendix

LEARNING STRATEGIES INVENTORY I

This learning strategies inventory will help you find out about your skills for learning. Think about what you do when studying. Then answer each question. There are no right or wrong answers.

When you finish, you will see where you are doing well. And you will find areas you need to work on. You will learn more about each area in this book.

Read each statement. Decide how true it is for you. Put an X in the box under "Very true for me," "Sometimes true for me," or "Not at all true for me."

	Very true for me	Sometimes true for me	Not at all true for me
Group 1			
1. I don't use learning strategies at home or work.			
2. I see no use for learning strategies when I finish school.			

	Very true for me	Sometimes true for me	Not at all true for me
Group 2			
3. I don't know my learning style.			
4. I don't know how to use my learning style to help me study.			
5. I think everyone learns the same way.			
6. I try to study the same way as my friends study.			

	Very true for me	Sometimes true for me	Not at all true for me
Group 3			
7. I see no purpose to my classes.			
8. I don't know what I want to do when I finish school.			
9. I have never thought about my goals.			

	Very true for me	Sometimes true for me	Not at all true for me
Group 4			
10. I forget deadlines and appointments.			
11. I don't have time to do what I need to do.			
12. I usually do papers or projects the night before they are due.			
13. I lose assignments or papers.			
14. I get to school without everything I need.			
15. I get interrupted a lot when I try to study.			
16. I often have to do assignments over.			
17. I often have to stop working to look for supplies.			
18. I watch television or talk on the phone when I study.			

	Very true for me	Sometimes true for me	Not at all true for me
Group 5			
19. I don't know where to find information I need.			
20. I have trouble finding information in the library.			
21. I can't find the information I need on the Internet.			
22. I have trouble finding information in my textbooks.			

	Very true for me	Sometimes true for me	Not at all true for me
Group 6			
23. I can't pick out the main idea in what I read.			
24. I'm not sure where to find meanings of words in my books.			
25. The index is hard for me to use.			
26. I skip over graphs and pictures when I read.			

Group 7	Very true for me	Sometimes true for me	Not at all true for me
27. I don't remember what I've read.			
28. I often read information but don't understand it.			
29. I do not know how to scan material.			
30. I have trouble picking out what is important in what I read.			

Group 8	Very true for me	Sometimes true for me	Not at all true for me
31. When I take notes, I try to write everything down.			
32. I can't always read my notes later.			
33. Taking notes does not seem to help me.			
34. I seem to have the wrong things in my notes.			
35. I'm not sure what to write when I take notes in class.			
36. It's hard to keep up when I take notes.			
37. I don't look over my notes after class.			

Group 9	Very true for me	Sometimes true for me	Not at all true for me
38. I need to learn to focus better when I study.			
39. I try to memorize definitions word for word.			
40. I listen in class, but I can't remember everything.			
41. It's hard for me to remember facts for a test.			
42. I get really nervous when I have to take a test.			
43. I need to learn how to remember better.			

	Very true for me	Sometimes true for me	Not at all true for me
Group 10			
44. Often I run out of time when I take a test.			
45. I need to learn to be a better test-taker.			
46. I spend hours cramming before a test.			
47. I do the hardest questions first on a test.			
48. I do poorly on essay tests.			
49. I make careless mistakes on true-false tests.			
50. I have lost points by not following directions on a test.			

By group, count the number of Xs you marked under "Very true for me" or "Sometimes true for me." Write that number in the chart below next to the correct group. The learning strategies covered by the groups are listed on the right. The higher the number of Xs, the more practice you need on that skill.

Group	Number of Xs marked	Skills covered in that group
1		Using learning strategies at school, home, and work
2		Using your learning style
3		Setting goals for yourself
4		Getting organized
5		Knowing where to find information
6		Knowing the parts of a book
7		Understanding what you read
8		Learning to take notes
9		Remembering what you learn
10		Being a better test-taker

Remember, work hard as you go through this book, and you will be rewarded at school, home, and work.

LEARNING STRATEGIES INVENTORY II

When you started using this book, you took a learning strategies inventory. Below is a second inventory. The purpose of this inventory is to help you examine your learning skills now that you have finished the book.

Read each statement. Decide how true it is for you. Put an X in the box under "Very true for me," "Sometimes true for me," or "Not at all true for me."

	Very true for me	Sometimes true for me	Not at all true for me
Group 1			
1. I use learning strategies at school, home, and work.			
2. I see uses for learning strategies when I finish school.			

	Very true for me	Sometimes true for me	Not at all true for me
Group 2			
3. I know my learning style.			
4. I know how to use my learning style to help me study.			
5. I understand that people learn in different ways.			
6. I try to study the way that is best for me.			

	Very true for me	Sometimes true for me	Not at all true for me
Group 3			
7. I have a purpose for learning in school.			
8. I have thought about what I want to do when I finish school.			
9. I have set some goals.			

	Very true for me	Sometimes true for me	Not at all true for me
Group 4			
10. I put deadlines and appointments on a calendar.			
11. I usually have time to do what I need to do.			
12. I usually do papers or projects over a period of several days before they are due.			
13. I write assignments in an assignment notebook.			
14. I get to school with everything I need.			
15. I rarely get interrupted when I study.			
16. I don't often have to do assignments over.			
17. I keep my supplies organized in my study spot.			
18. I don't watch television or talk on the phone when I study.			

	Very true for me	Sometimes true for me	Not at all true for me
Group 5			
19. I know where to find information I need.			
20. I can find information in the library.			
21. I can narrow down information on the Internet.			
22. I can find information in my textbooks.			

	Very true for me	Sometimes true for me	Not at all true for me
Group 6			
23. I can pick out the main idea in what I read.			
24. I know how to use the glossary.			
25. I know how to use an index to find information.			
26. I read and understand graphs and visual aids.			

	Very true for me	Sometimes true for me	Not at all true for me
Group 7			
27. I remember more of what I've read.			
28. I read information and understand it.			
29. I know how to scan material.			
30. I can pick out what is important in what I read.			

	Very true for me	Sometimes true for me	Not at all true for me
Group 8			
31. When I take notes, I try to write the main points.			
32. I can read my notes later.			
33. Taking notes helps me.			
34. I usually have the right things in my notes.			
35. I know what to write when I take notes in class.			
36. I use abbreviations and symbols when I take notes.			
37. I look over my notes after class.			

	Very true for me	Sometimes true for me	Not at all true for me
Group 9			
38. I focus better when I study.			
39. I write definitions in my own words.			
40. I listen in class and try to write down the main points.			
41. I am learning to remember facts for a test.			
42. I am more confident when I have to take a test.			
43. I know how to use some memory aids to help me remember better.			

	Very true for me	Sometimes true for me	Not at all true for me
Group 10			
44. I plan my time when I take a test.			
45. I am learning to be a better test-taker.			
46. I don't cram before a test. I study over a period of time.			
47. I do the easiest questions first on a test.			
48. I do well on essay tests.			
49. I avoid careless mistakes on true-false tests.			
50. I don't lose points by not following directions on a test.			

Count the number of Xs you marked in each group under "Not at all true for me." Write that number in the chart for that group. Read what skill is covered by that group in the inventory.

Group	Number of Xs marked	Skills covered in that group
1		Using learning strategies at school, home, and work
2		Using your learning style
3		Setting goals for yourself
4		Getting organized
5		Knowing where to find information
6		Knowing the parts of a book
7		Understanding what you read
8		Learning to take notes
9		Remembering what you learn
10		Being a better test-taker

If you marked "Not at all true of me" for two or more items in a group, you need to review the chapter that teaches about the skills in that group.

If you marked one or zero items in a group, you are well on your way to mastering that skill. Remember: Practice makes perfect. Keep using your learning skills until they become learning habits. You will find they will make your life better!

REMEMBERING THE MAIN IDEAS

Let's review some of the most important ideas in *Learning Strategies for School, Home, and Work*. These ideas were marked throughout the book with the lightbulb symbol.

GETTING STARTED: USING YOUR LEARNING STYLE

- You may be a visual, auditory, or kinesthetic learner.
- Visual learners learn best by seeing the information they need to learn.
- Auditory learners learn best by hearing information they need to learn.
- Kinesthetic learners learn best by doing.

CHAPTER 1: SETTING GOALS FOR YOURSELF

- A goal should be important, specific, and realistic.
- Short-term goals can be reached in short periods of time. Long-term goals take months or years to reach.
- Write down your goal and the steps needed to reach it. Put the paper where you will see it daily.
- A long-term goal must be broken into steps.

CHAPTER 2: GETTING ORGANIZED

- A To Do list will help you get things done.
- A schedule will help you use your time well and work toward your goals.
- A calendar will help you remember dates and deadlines.
- Jobs at school, home, and work will go better if you organize your space.
- Wasting time can keep you from getting a job done.

CHAPTER 3: KNOWING WHERE TO GET INFORMATION

- The telephone book has information to help you solve many problems.
- The newspaper has up-to-date information on many topics.
- The librarian can help you use the resources of the library.
- Reference books give you basic information on many topics.
- Library books are organized by call number.
- Narrow your search to get the information you need on the Internet.
- Other people have good information to share if you are willing to ask.

CHAPTER 4: GETTING INFORMATION FROM BOOKS

- You can get more out of a book if you know how to use its parts.
- The table of contents lists chapter names and main topics.
- An index tells the pages where topics in the book can be found.
- Visual aids often give information not found in the text.
- A pie chart shows the relationship of parts to the whole.

CHAPTER 5: UNDERSTANDING WHAT YOU READ

- The three steps to Active Reading are scan, read, and review.
- Scanning gives you the main idea of the material.
- Turn each heading into a question as you read.
- Reviewing after you read will help you remember better.

CHAPTER 6: LEARNING TO TAKE NOTES

- Active listeners hear and try to understand what is being said.
- Taking notes will help you remember what you hear.
- Following the clues will help you take more complete notes.
- Using abbreviations and symbols will help you take notes faster.
- Go over your notes as soon as you can after you take them and rewrite them if needed.

CHAPTER 7: REMEMBERING WHAT YOU LEARN

- Make sure you understand the meaning of a new word, then review it often to learn it.
- Taking notes will help you remember what you read.
- To memorize a longer passage, break it into parts and learn one part at a time.
- Using repetition and mind pictures can help you remember.
- Put facts into groups or think of rhymes to help you remember.
- Use acronyms and association to help you remember.

CHAPTER 8: BEING A BETTER TEST-TAKER

- Being prepared is the most important part of good test-taking.
- Look over the test before you begin and plan your time.
- Read each statement on a true-false test very carefully.
- On a matching test, read all items in both columns before making any matches. On a fill-in test, read over your answers to make sure they make sense.
- On a multiple-choice test, read all the choices before you choose.
- Pay attention to direction words in answering essay questions.
- Practice tests can help you prepare for standardized tests.

WEB SITES

The following web sites provide additional information on study skills:

www.ucc.vt.edu/studysk/stdyhllp.html This site contains self-help information on study skills, including on-line study-skills interactive workshops.

www.mindtools.com The goal of this web site is to help you understand the essential skills (including study skills) that will help you excel in your career.

www.mtsu.edu/~studskl This study-skills help page contains great tips on studying and test-taking.

www.gradebook.org The section called The Classroom has many tips on test-taking and study skills.

www.how-to-study.com This site has excellent, easy-to-read suggestions for developing better listening, reading, note-taking, and other study skills.

www.iss.stthomas.edu/studyguides This offers a step-by-step guide that teaches students to study and prepare for tests. It includes a special section for those with ADD or ADHD.

www.eyesoftime.com. The School Page has links to study-skills sites.

www.arc.sbc.edu/studylinks.html This site has information on a large variety of study skills and an on-line study-skills assessment.

www.icpac.indiana.edu/publications/planners/studyskills/index This site has a downloadable study-skills booklet covering a wide range of skills.

www.berghuis.co.nz/abiator/lsi/lsiframe.html This site contains Abiator's Online Learning Inventory. Two self-testing instruments show you how you prefer to learn (visual, auditory, or kinesthetic). After you find your style, you can get more information about learning strengths and strategies.

Share Your Bright Ideas

We want to hear from you!

Your name_____Date_____

School name_____

School address_____

City _____State _____Zip_____Phone number (_____)_____

Grade level(s) taught_____Subject area(s) taught_____

Where did you purchase this publication?_____

In what month do you purchase a majority of your supplements?_____

What moneys were used to purchase this product?

_____School supplemental budget _____Federal/state funding _____Personal

Please "grade" this Walch publication in the following areas:

Quality of service you received when purchasing ....A   B   C   D

Ease of use..A   B   C   D

Quality of content..A   B   C   D

Page layout ....A   B   C   D

Organization of material ....A   B   C   D

Suitability for grade level...A   B   C   D

Instructional value...A   B   C   D

COMMENTS:_____

_____

What specific supplemental materials would help you meet your current—or future—instructional needs?

_____

Have you used other Walch publications? If so, which ones?_____

May we use your comments in upcoming communications?   _____Yes   _____No

Please **FAX** this completed form to **888-991-5755**, or mail it to

Customer Service, J. Weston Walch, Publisher, P. O. Box 658, Portland, ME 04104-0658

We will send you a **FREE GIFT** in appreciation of your feedback. **THANK YOU!**